Grammar and Language Links

ELEMENTS OF
Literature
INTRODUCTORY COURSE

WORKSHEETS
ANSWER KEY

HOLT, RINEHART AND WINSTON
Harcourt Brace & Company

Austin • New York • Orlando • Atlanta • San Francisco • Boston • Dallas • Toronto • London

Staff Credits

Associate Director: Mescal Evler

Manager of Editorial Operations: Robert R. Hoyt

Managing Editor: Bill Wahlgren

Project Editor: Katie Vignery

Component Editor: Scott Hall

Editorial Staff: *Associate Editors,* Kathryn Rogers, Christopher LeCluyse; *Assistant Managing Editor,* Mandy Beard; *Copyediting Supervisor,* Michael Neibergall; *Senior Copyeditor,* Mary Malone; *Copyeditors,* Joel Bourgeois, Jeffrey T. Holt, Jane Kominek; *Editorial Coordinators,* Marie H. Price, Robert Littlefield, Mark Holland, Jill O'Neal, Marcus Johnson, Tracy DeMont; *Support Staff,* Pat Stover, Matthew Villalobos; *Word Processors,* Ruth Hooker, Margaret Sanchez, Kelly Keeley

Permissions: Tamara A. Blanken, Ann B. Farrar

Design: *Art Director, Book Design,* Richard Metzger; *Design Manager, Book & Media Design,* Joe Melomo

Prepress Production: Beth Prevelige, Simira Davis, Sergio Durante

Manufacturing Coordinator: Michael Roche

Printed in the United States of America

ISBN 0-03-052354-0

7 8 9 10 11 12 022 07 06 05 04 03 02

TABLE OF CONTENTS

COLLECTION EIGHT:
TELL ME A TALE

The copying masters in this *Grammar and Language Links* booklet correspond to the Grammar Link and Language Link features, which follow the selections in the Pupil's Edition. These copying masters provide reinforcement, practice, and extension of the grammar and language skills presented in those features. Integrating language study with literature, worksheet examples and activities generally refer to the content of the selections. These features are included with the activities that follow the selections.

The page number of the corresponding Grammar Link or Language Link feature in the Pupil's Edition is referenced on the copying masters for each selection.

ANSWER KEY

The Answer Key provides answers to all objective questions in *Grammar and Language Links,* as well as models or guidelines for responses to open-ended questions and activities.

GRAMMAR LINK

Just Once
Thomas J. Dygard

Troublesome Verbs

Everybody could benefit by using verb tenses correctly. The Moose in "Just Once" doesn't say much. However, when he does talk, he uses verbs correctly. Maybe part of the reason people listen to him is that they respect him.

These regular verbs form their past tense and past participle by adding *-d* or *-ed* to the base form. The past participle is used to form each of the perfect tenses.

Present	Past	Past Participle
like	liked	(have) liked
block	blocked	(have) blocked
call	called	(have) called

Unlike regular verbs, **irregular verbs** can be tricky. Instead of adding *-d* or *-ed*, these verbs form the past and past participle in some other way.

There are many irregular verbs. The following chart gives the tense forms of ten irregular verbs from "Just Once."

Present	Past	Past Participle
come	came	(have) come
do	did	(have) done
get	got	(have) gotten *or* got
give	gave	(have) given
go	went	(have) gone
know	knew	(have) known
make	made	(have) made
run	ran	(have) run
see	saw	(have) seen
win	won	(have) won

In informal situations, people often use nonstandard verb tense forms. However, in formal speech and writing, it is important to use standard verb tense forms.

Avoid the following common errors when forming the past or past participle of irregular verbs.

1. Don't use the past form with the helping verb *has* or *have*.

    NONSTANDARD: He has went to the locker room.

    STANDARD: He has **gone** to the locker room.

2. Don't use the past participle without a helping verb.

    NONSTANDARD: The Moose done his job well.

    STANDARD: The Moose **had** done his job well.

3. Don't add *-d* or *-ed* to the base form of an irregular verb to form the past tense.

    NONSTANDARD: The players in red jerseys runned to tackle the Moose.

    STANDARD: The players in red jerseys **ran** to tackle the Moose.

EXERCISE A Forming the Past and Past Perfect Tenses

Read each of the following sentences. On the blank provided, write the correct form of the verb in parentheses. All sentences should be in the past or past perfect tense.

    EXAMPLE: Bedford City High had (*win*) the game!   *won*
_____

1. Everybody on the team (*do*) his job well.   _____

2. The coach had (*give*) the Moose a chance.   _____

3. We (*know*) he could do it.   _____

4. The Moose had (*make*) a touchdown!   _____

5. You should have (*see*) the look on the coach's face.   _____

EXERCISE B Proofreading Paragraphs

Proofread the following paragraphs for errors in verb tense forms. Cross out each incorrect verb form, and write the correct form above it. The first correction has been made for you. Find five more.

                                        given

    Some other linemen, like us, had also ~~gived~~ some thought to carrying the ball. We just stayed quiet and gone about our business. However, after the Moose had went to the coach, we discussed the issue. We seen both points of view—the coach's and the Moose's.

    We're glad that the Moose gotten his chance because it was our chance, too. Also, we have came to realize that everybody has something he or she does best, and we're going to keep on blocking.

GRAMMAR LINK

Ta-Na-E-Ka
Mary Whitebird

Subjects and Verbs—In Perfect Agreement

> Mary and Roger **deal** with Ta-Na-E-Ka in different ways.
> Hunger or a hamburger **awaits** Mary on the first day of her ritual.

Both sentences above have compound subjects (*Mary and Roger, hunger or a hamburger*). However, the number of the verb in the first sentence is plural (*deal*), and the number of the verb in the second sentence is singular (*awaits*). Why is there a difference? The chart below will explain the difference. [Hint: Notice that the subjects in the first sentence above are joined by *and,* while the subjects in the second sentence are joined by *or.*]

Rule	Example
Subjects joined by the word *and* take a plural verb.	Roger **and** Mary **feel** anxious about Ta-Na-E-Ka. [The plural verb *feel* agrees with the plural subject *Roger and Mary.*]
Singular subjects joined by *or* or *nor* take a singular verb.	Neither Roger **nor** Mary **was** looking forward to Ta-Na-E-Ka. [The singular verb *was* agrees with the singular subjects *Mary* and *Roger.*]
When a singular subject and a plural subject are joined by *or* or *nor,* the verb agrees with the subject that is nearer to the verb.	If necessary, an edible root **or** some wild berries **prevent** starving. [The plural verb *prevent* agrees with the plural subject *berries.*]

EXERCISE A **Compound Subject-Verb Agreement**

Read each sentence below, and circle the verb in parentheses that agrees with the subject.

EXAMPLE: To prepare for Ta-Na-E-Ka, Roger and Mary (*learns,* (*learn*)) many things.

1. Eating grasshoppers and digging for roots (*is, are*) part of Roger's Ta-Na-E-Ka.

2. A different era and a new attitude (*demands, demand*) different skills.

3. Folklore or tradition (*preserve, preserves*) old knowledge.

4. Tradition or its lessons (*teach, teaches*) values to those who are willing to learn.

5. Neither a grasshopper nor crickets (*was, were*) appetizing to Mary.

EXERCISE B Proofreading Paragraphs

The following paragraphs contain errors in subject-verb agreement. Correct the errors by crossing out the incorrect verbs and writing the correct forms above the mistakes. Read carefully—not every sentence contains an error. One correction has been made for you as an example.

Historically, the attitudes and traditions of many cultures ~~allows~~ *allow* for a different treatment of men and women, boys and girls. However, in "Ta-Na-E-Ka," we see a culture in which neither males nor females receives preferential treatment.

Roger's parents, Mary's parents, and Roger and Mary's grandfather agrees that Ta-Na-E-Ka is an important tradition. Grandfather and the parents needs to compromise, though, because they disagree on some parts of the tradition. They end up with a fair agreement.

Mary and Roger choose which part of the woods they will claim. Mary stays by the river while Roger goes into the woods. At that point, intelligence or traditions becomes the key to survival. In the end, Mary breaks with tradition, but Grandfather shows that both he and his traditions is flexible.

EXERCISE C Sentence Completion

On each of the lines below, add words to the compound subject to make a complete sentence. Be sure that the subject and verb agree.

EXAMPLE: The marina and the restaurant
The marina and the restaurant help Mary survive. _____

1. Mary and Roger

_____

2. An insect or berries

_____

3. Neither Roger, Mary's parents, nor Grandfather

_____

4. Mary's teacher and Ernie from the restaurant

_____

GRAMMAR LINK

The All-American Slurp
Lensey Namioka   Pupil's Edition page 43

Subject-Verb Agreement and the Search for the Subject

> A plate of vegetables was served.
> Are many stalks of celery left on the plate?

In some sentences, the subject seems to be hiding. At first glance, it is difficult to tell whether the subject in the first sentence is *plate* or *vegetables.* In the second sentence, the verb *are* doesn't follow the subject. With what subject should the verb agree? In cases like these, determining subject-verb agreement can be difficult.

Here are some tips to help you.

Tip 1: For a question in which the verb comes before the noun, rearrange the question to make a statement.

  QUESTION: Is the dip on the table?
  STATEMENT: The *dip* is on the table.

[After changing the question to a statement, it's easy to see that the subject of the sentence is *dip.*]

Tip 2: The subject is never in a prepositional phrase. (A prepositional phrase begins with a preposition, such as *around, for, in, of, on, toward,* or *with,* and ends with a noun or pronoun.) When you are looking for the subject, try leaving out any prepositional phrases as you read the sentence.

  WITH PREPOSITIONAL PHRASE: A plate of vegetables was served.
  WITHOUT PREPOSITIONAL PHRASE: A **plate** was served.

[When you leave out the prepositional phrase *of vegetables,* it's easy to see that *plate* is the subject of the sentence.]

EXERCISE A Finding the Subjects in Questions

Answer each of the following questions by writing a complete sentence. You may add words so that the sentence makes sense. Then, in the original question, circle the correct form of the verb in parentheses.

  EXAMPLE: How long (*have*, *has*) the Lins been in the country?
  The Lins have been in the country for a short time.

1. Why (*are*, *is*) eating rituals different in different cultures?

2. Where (*is, are*) the chopsticks?

Elements of Literature   *Grammar and Language Link Worksheets* **5**

3. (*Was, Were*) the parents enjoying the meal?

_____

4. Where (*are, is*) the rice and prawns?

_____

5. (*Has, Have*) you ever been embarrassed while eating?

_____

EXERCISE B **Identifying Subjects**

For each of the following sentences, underline the subject. Then, circle the correct form of the verb in parentheses.

EXAMPLE: The <u>stalks</u> of celery ((look), *looks*) delicious.

1. Food in different countries (*is, are*) prepared differently.

2. Specialties from another culture often (*taste, tastes*) delicious.

3. Meals from around the world (*differ, differs*) in presentation.

4. The ingredients in this dish (*is, are*) not suited for everyone.

5. The food of other cultures (*is, are*) a treat for adventurous eaters.

EXERCISE C **Proofreading a Paragraph**

The following paragraph contains verbs that don't agree with their subjects. Cross out each incorrect verb, and write the correct form above it. The first verb has been corrected. Find and correct the other five errors.

Students in schools across the nation *get* ~~gets~~ embarrassed easily. Have an embarrassing

thing happened to you? One of the most likely places are the cafeteria. Your friends tell

jokes, sometimes right after you take a big swallow of milk. Has you ever dropped a tray full

of food? The cafeteria in most schools are the stage of many such scenes. Sometimes acci-

dents in a cafeteria is hazardous to your ego.

GRAMMAR LINK

La Bamba
Gary Soto

Using Verb Tenses

What is the difference between the way Manuel and Benny use the boldfaced verbs in the following dialogue?

> MANUEL: I **thought** that Petra Lopez wouldn't notice me unless I performed at the talent contest.
>
> BENNY: I **think** that you don't have to worry anymore!

If you think the difference is between present tense and past tense, you're right! The **tense** of a verb indicates the time of the action or the state of being expressed by the verb.

PRESENT:	(existing or happening now): Manuel **thinks.**
PAST:	(existing or happening in the past): Manuel **thought.**
FUTURE:	(existing or happening in the future): Manuel **will think.**
PRESENT PERFECT:	(existing or happening sometime before now): Manuel **has thought.**
PAST PERFECT:	(existing or happening before a specific time in the past): Manuel **had thought.**
FUTURE PERFECT:	(existing or happening before a specific time in the future): Manuel **will have thought.**

When you're writing, an important thing to remember about using tenses is to be consistent. Generally, if you start in the past tense, stay in it. Don't switch unnecessarily from past to present tense, or from present to past tense.

SWITCHED TENSES:	When Manuel arrived at school, he realizes he didn't have his math workbook.
CONSISTENT TENSES:	When Manuel *arrived* at school, he *realized* he didn't have his math workbook.

EXERCISE A Identifying Verb Tenses

Underline the verb or verbs in each of the following sentences. Then, on the lines provided, write the tenses of the verbs.

EXAMPLE: Mr. Roybal had broken the student's fall. _past perfect_

1. Manuel walked to school in the cold morning. _____

2. He kicks leaves up into the air. _____

3. He had raised his hand in front of the class. _____

4. Benny has practiced his trumpet playing despite a fat lip. _____

5. Manuel's father knew his son had a secret. _____

6. His mother will have seen his performance by tomorrow. _____

7. The audience laughs at the toothbrush and the dirty tooth. _____

8. Benny will volunteer for the talent show next year. _____

9. I had played hopscotch with Petra in elementary school. _____

10. She will have graduated by now. _____

EXERCISE B **Revising a Paragraph**

The following paragraph contains errors in the use of verb tenses. As you identify each error, cross out the incorrect word and write the correct tense of the verb above it. One error is identified and corrected as an example. Find ten more.

When I was in the sixth grade, I ~~perform~~ *performed* in a talent contest. I decided to play the school

song on my guitar. I practiced almost every day before the show so that I know the song as

well as I knew my name. The night of the show, everybody except me acts nervous. I walk

around backstage and tapped kids on the shoulders, and they jump. The first performer tap-

danced in a red tutu. Halfway through the routine, one of her heels flew off. The dancer

keeps right on dancing. The second performer is Jamal, a buddy of mine. He read a few

haiku that he wrote himself. He received a huge round of applause when he finished. Finally,

I hear my name announced. I grabbed my guitar and jumped up on stage. Then I launched

into the song. I took a deep breath. Just as I am ready to sing the first line, one of my strings

broke, and it popped me on my upper lip. "Ow!" I yell. People were stunned. After a few

seconds, I started to sing, but my upper lip was numb, and only nonsense words came out!

The audience did not know how to respond. I finally gave up and stalk off the stage.

LANGUAGE LINK

President Cleveland, Where Are You?
Robert Cormier   Pupil's Edition page 68

Style: Actions Speak Louder with Vivid Verbs

With the Grover Cleveland card in mind, Armand and I fixed the bike tire in just minutes. Armand stood amazed as I got back onto the seat and rode off to the North Side Drugstore.

With the Grover Cleveland card in mind, Armand and I **tore** the bike tire down and **patched** the leak in just minutes. Armand stood amazed as I **leapt** back onto the seat, **zigged** into traffic, and **disappeared** toward the North Side Drugstore.

Which paragraph is more exciting to read? Which one helps you better understand Jerry's urgency to get to the store? The second paragraph is better because it uses **vivid verbs** rather than vague verbs. A **verb** is a word that expresses an *action* or a *state of being*. The left side of the chart below lists three vague verbs; the right side lists some more vivid substitutes.

Vague	Vivid
eat	gobble, devour
take	grab, snatch
turn	whirl, spin

Many writers focus on nouns and modifiers (adjectives and adverbs) to tell a story. While these word types help create a pretty picture, they can't breathe life into a story by themselves. **Verbs** can enliven, electrify, and energize sentences and can help the writer grab the reader's attention.

EXERCISE A   Identifying Vivid Verbs

Circle the verb or verbs in each of the following sentences. In the blank(s) provided, identify each verb as **vivid** or **vague.**

EXAMPLE: We often (clustered) in front of Lemire's Drugstore.   _____vivid_____

1. Rollie Tremaine risked Ken Maynards only when we

   threatened to avoid him.   _____

2. I went through the screen door in a hurry.   _____

3. Albert snorted the name Ken Maynard with contempt.   _____

4. We rode our bicycles through the streets.   _____

5. Spring exploded with blossoms and fragrances.   _____

EXERCISE B **Writing with Vivid Verbs**

Quickly write a five-sentence paragraph describing a Frenchtown Tigers baseball game, Armand's date with Sally at the dance, or Jerry selling the Grover Cleveland card to Rollie Tremaine.

_____

_____

_____

_____

_____

_____

_____

_____

Now, go back and underline the verbs in your paragraph. In the space below, list five vague verbs you would like to change. Then, for each vague verb, use your imagination or a thesaurus to write three **vivid verbs** that could replace the vague verb.

Vague Verbs	Vivid Verbs		
1.			
2.			
3.			
4.			
5.			

Now, go back to the original paragraph. Cross out each vague verb, and replace it with one of your vivid verbs.

Trade paragraphs with a partner. On the lines provided, explain how using **vivid verbs** improved your partner's paragraph by creating more lively imagery and expressing more emotion.

_____

_____

_____

_____

_____

The Stone
Lloyd Alexander

Pupil's Edition page 81

Watch Your *Don't*s and *Doesn't*s

In the course of this collection, you have learned and practiced most of the rules for making verbs agree with subjects. Here are a few last tips for you to follow. If you **don't** get all the rules right away, don't worry. It **doesn't** mean you *can't* get them; it just means you need to keep practicing!

With	Use	Examples
Singular subjects except the singular pronouns *I* and *you*	• doesn't • is	• **She doesn't** like it. • **He is** making a wish.
Plural subjects and the singular pronoun *you*	• don't • are	• **We don't** want it. • **You don't** want it? • **They are** keeping the stone. • **You are** making a wish.
The pronoun *I*	• don't • am	• **I don't** want the stone. • **I am** making a wish.

Here are some tips to help with unusual cases in which it's difficult to tell whether the subject is singular or plural.

Rule	Example
Words and phrases giving **amounts** are usually singular.	• Fifty million dollars **is** a lot of money. • Ten ounces of gold **is** worth a lot of money.
Titles of creative works and **names of groups and organizations** are usually singular.	• "The Bare Necessities" **is** my favorite song. • Wishers Anonymous **is** a support group for people addicted to wishing.
A few nouns, like *chickenpox, news,* and *mathematics,* are plural in form but take singular verbs.	• Chickenpox **is** a disease. • Mathematics **is** my favorite subject.

EXERCISE A   Identifying the Correct Verb Form

Circle the verb form in parentheses that agrees with the subject.

EXAMPLE: Shelby (*don't,* (*doesn't*)) believe that dwarfs can give you wishes.

1. She (*don't, doesn't*)?

2. A dwarf (*don't, doesn't*) give a wish unless he or she needs a favor.

3. Wishes (*don't, doesn't*) count for much, though.

4. Unless you're very careful, (*don't*, *doesn't*) wishes usually backfire?

5. I (*don't*, *doesn't*) think wishing is worth the risk.

EXERCISE B **Choosing Verbs That Agree with Their Subjects**

Circle the verb form that agrees with the subject.

> **EXAMPLE:** The evening news (*are*, (*is*)) doing a feature on wishes tonight.

1. One hundred pounds (*is*, *are*) heavy for one of the Fair Folk.

2. Three hundred fifty million dollars (*buy*, *buys*) many books.

3. Teachers Against Illiteracy (*don't*, *doesn't*) support the senator's plan.

4. *The Fish's Dishes* (*is*, *are*) my sister's favorite book.

5. The measles (*is*, *are*) a disease for which a vaccine is available.

EXERCISE C **Proofreading Paragraphs**

The following conversation could have taken place between Maibon and the dwarf if things had worked out differently. The conversation contains errors in the agreement of subjects and verbs. As you identify each error, cross out the verb and write the correct form above it. One error is identified and corrected as an example. Find and correct ten more.

> don't
> "I ~~doesn't~~ understand why you don't want the stone any longer, Maibon."

> "My wife don't like the way I is now that I have power over my aging. The kids is scared of me, too. They doesn't understand why they and their mother keep growing older while I don't get any older at all."

> "I'll tell you what I am willing to do since you is in such a predicament. *Little Sellers Weekly* are a newspaper the Fair Folk put out each week. I doesn't know of a better place to run an ad for the stone. We is going to tell the virtues of the stone and set the price at one thousand dollars."

> "One thousand dollars are a fortune! I doesn't think we are going to get a buyer with that price, but we are going to have to try. The ad is our only hope."

GRAMMAR LINK

Storm
Gary Paulsen   Pupil's Edition page 107

Using *Good* and *Well* Correctly

JOSH: Mr. Bailey read us a good short story about a man and his dog.

KAREN: Why did you like the story so much?

JOSH: The dog was very smart, and besides, Mr. Bailey reads well.

Did you notice how Josh used *good* and *well* differently? Many people get confused about which word to use in a particular situation. In Josh's first statement, he uses *good* to describe the noun *story*. His second statement uses *well* to modify the verb *reads*. Think about what word *good* or *well* modifies, and you will know which one to use.

Good is an adjective and should be used to modify only a *noun* or a *pronoun*.

I think that Storm had a **good** owner. [*Good* describes the noun *owner*.]

He was **good** because he worked hard. [*Good* describes the pronoun *He*.]

Well is usually an adverb, and should be used to modify a *verb*, an *adjective*, or another *adverb*.

Storm and the team of dogs pulled the sled **well**. [*Well* describes the verb *pulled*, telling *how* Storm and the team pulled.]

Paulsen is an author who is **well** loved by young readers. [*Well* describes the participle *loved*, telling how loved Paulsen is. (A participle is a verb form that can be used as an adjective.)]

Well can also be used as an adjective, meaning "healthy."

I am very **well**, thank you. [The adjective *well* describes the subject *I*.]

Be careful! In standard English, **good** should never be used to modify a verb.

NONSTANDARD: Paulsen did good in the Iditarod, the famous sled race.

STANDARD: Paulsen did **well** in the Iditarod, the famous sled race.

A Special Case: *Feel*

Feel good and *feel well* mean very different things. *Feel good* means "to feel happy or pleased."

Paulsen **felt good** about Storm's winning performance in the sled race.
[Here, Paulsen is pleased because Storm won a race.]

Feel well means "to feel healthy."

After the long trip, the dog was hungry and did not **feel well**. [Here, the trip has affected the dog's health.]

EXERCISE A Using *Good* and *Well* Correctly

In each of the following sentences, underline the word that correctly completes the sentence.

    EXAMPLE: Paulsen's sled glided (*good, well*) and helped him to move fast.

1. Though Storm played tricks on his owner, he was still a (*good, well*) dog.

2. Storm ran (*good, well*), and Paulsen's team went on to victory.

3. Storm did very (*good, well*) in the race, and as a result, he was awarded a prize.

4. Because Storm did such a (*good, well*) job in the Iditarod, Paulsen gave him a treat.

5. Though he had the flu, Paulsen felt (*good, well*) about winning the race.

EXERCISE B Proofreading Paragraphs

The following paragraphs contain errors in the use of *good* and *well.* Correct each error by crossing it out and writing the correct word above it. One correction has been made for you. Find and correct five more errors.

                      good
    I have another ~~well~~ story about my dog Storm. We had just done really good in a big race, and I was exhausted. I had been sick for several days and still was not feeling good. I sat in a big, comfortable chair in the corner of my cabin. I had built a fire that did a good job of keeping me warm. As I sat and tried to rest, I heard a rustling at the window. I did not feel good about the sound. The wind howled. I quietly called out, "Storm? Storm? Are you there?"

    I waited silently, and I looked through the window. I saw a brown stocking cap moving outside. The wind moaned, and I had a sinking feeling inside me. The situation was not well. Suddenly, Storm came through the door, giving me a good scare. He held my hunting hat in his mouth. I had a good laugh. It had only been Storm outside playing a prank. He had certainly tricked me good. I was relieved, so I got out of my chair and went to the kitchen. I got Storm a treat. He had earned it good.

LANGUAGE LINK

Brother
Maya Angelou   **Pupil's Edition page 116**

Style: Choosing Precise Words

> **DEVEN:**   Bailey was a good brother to Maya Angelou.
>
> **SULEE:**   What do you mean?
>
> **DEVEN:**   He was supportive, reassuring, and humorous.

How is Deven's first statement about Bailey different from his second? In his first description of Bailey, Deven uses the modifier *good.* A **modifier** is a word, a phrase, or a clause that describes or limits the meaning of another word. *Good* is a **general modifier.** It is vague and doesn't give a precise picture of Bailey. In Deven's second statement, he uses the words *supportive, reassuring,* and *humorous.* These are **specific modifiers** that present a more exact picture.

General Modifiers

Words such as *good* and *pretty* are **general modifiers.** Because they are vague, they give only a hint of what the author really means. Look at the following sentence.

> Bailey thinks that pickles taste good. [What exactly does Bailey like about pickles?]

Specific Modifiers

Specific modifiers are more accurate words that invoke precise images. Compare the above sentence about Bailey to the one below.

> Bailey likes pickles because they taste **salty** and have a **crunchy** texture.

EXERCISE A   Thesaurus Rex

Thesaurus Rex hates general modifiers so much that he eats them at every opportunity. When he exhales, he breathes out specific modifiers. Each dinosaur below contains a general modifier. For each of these, use a dictionary or thesaurus to find two specific modifiers. One has been done for you.

EXAMPLE:

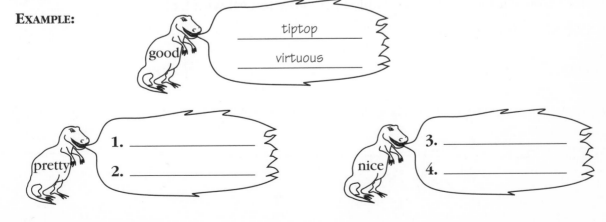

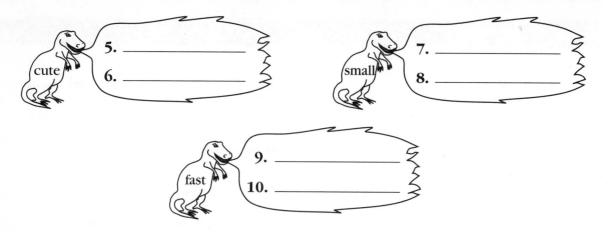

cute
5. _____
6. _____

small
7. _____
8. _____

fast
9. _____
10. _____

EXERCISE B **Revising Paragraphs**

The paragraphs below (which were not written by Maya Angelou) contain many general modifiers. Wherever you see a general modifier in italics, cross it out and write a more specific modifier in the space above it. You may use a thesaurus or a dictionary for this activity. One revision has been made for you.

I think that my brother Bailey is a *clever* ~~smart~~ person. He is very coordinated. He can steal

pickles from the store when no one is looking. One time Momma caught him with his hand

in the pickle barrel. She asked him, "Bailey, what are you doing at the pickle barrel?"

Bailey gulped. He thought quickly. "The *pretty* lady over by that *thin* man asked for a

pickle. I just wanted to help her."

Momma knew that Bailey was lying. Momma is also clever. The woman paid for her gro-

ceries. Momma packed everything the woman bought into one *large* bag. She then asked

Bailey, "Bailey, why don't you help Mrs. Coleman carry her groceries up that *high* hill?"

Bailey's eyes got *big*. Momma certainly knew how to deal with Bailey.

The Mysterious Mr. Lincoln
Russell Freedman   Pupil's Edition page 135

Comparing with Adjectives

> **OTIS:** Lincoln was the **best** president that the United States has ever had.
>
> **LITA:** What about George Washington?
>
> **OTIS:** I think that Lincoln was a **better** president than Washington was.

How is Otis's first statement different from his second? In Otis's first statement, he compares Lincoln to all the presidents that the United States has ever had. The word *best* is the *superlative* form of the adjective *good*. It is used when three or more items are compared. In Otis's second statement, he compares only two people, so he uses *better,* the *comparative* form of the adjective *good*. Below are some rules to keep in mind when making comparisons.

Using the Comparative and Superlative Forms

The three degrees of comparison of adjectives are positive, comparative, and superlative.

- Use the comparative degree when comparing two things.

   The North won the Civil War partly because it had **better** equipment than the South. [*Better* compares the equipment of the North and of the South.]

   At first, it was **more important** for Lincoln to preserve the Union than to abolish slavery. [*More important* compares two of Lincoln's war priorities, preserving the Union and abolishing slavery.]

- Use the superlative degree when comparing three or more things.

   Lincoln thought Grant was his **best** general. [*Best* compares Grant to all of Lincoln's other generals.]

   Of his four sons, Robert, Edward, William, and Tad, Lincoln was **closest** to Tad. [*Closest* compares Lincoln's relationship to Tad with his relationship to his other three sons.]

Be careful! Avoid making double comparisons. To form a comparison, do not use both the *–er* ending and *more* or *less* in front of a word. Likewise, do not use both the *–est* ending and *most* or *least* in front of a word.

NONSTANDARD: Lincoln was more taller than many other presidents in American history.

STANDARD: Lincoln was **taller** than many other presidents in American history.

Regular Comparison

Most one-syllable adjectives and some two-syllable adjectives form their comparative and superlative degrees by adding *–er* and *–est.*

Positive	Comparative	Superlative
high simple	higher simpler	highest simplest

Some two-syllable adjectives and all adjectives with three or more syllables form their comparative and superlative degrees by using *more* or *most.*

Positive	Comparative	Superlative
loyal	more loyal	most loyal
difficult	more difficult	most difficult

Irregular Comparison

Some adjectives do not form their comparative and superlative degrees in the regular way.

Positive	Comparative	Superlative
bad	worse	worst
good	better	best
little	less	least
many	more	most

EXERCISE A Using Comparative and Superlative Forms of Adjectives

In each sentence below, underline the correct adjective form.

EXAMPLE: Lincoln was the (*thinner, thinnest*) one in his family.

1. Compared to his rival, Lincoln was the (*better, best*) speaker.

2. At first, Lincoln thought preserving the Union was (*more, most*) important than freeing those who were enslaved.

3. During the Civil War, Lincoln was the (*less, least*) popular of any president ever elected.

4. The presidency is the (*higher, highest*) office in the land.

5. Of the two candidates, Lincoln was (*less, least*) well known.

EXERCISE B Proofreading Paragraphs

The following paragraphs contain errors in the use of comparative and superlative forms of adjectives. Cross out each incorrect modifier, and write the correct form in the space above it. One error has been corrected for you. Find and correct five more.

Abraham Lincoln was one of the ~~greater~~ *greatest* presidents that this country has ever had. He led

this country through one of the difficultest times in its history. Lincoln made two of the most

importantest contributions to the country: preserving the Union and abolishing slavery.

Although Lincoln was against slavery, it was not until after the war began that he

thought ending slavery was the more important of all war objectives. He issued the

Emancipation Proclamation, which officially freed many slaves. Unfortunately, soon after the

war, Lincoln was killed. The man who, during the war, was the most unpopularest president

of all time has come to be considered one of the better presidents in U.S. history.

GRAMMAR LINK

A Glory over Everything
Ann Petry   Pupil's Edition page 149

Don't Use *Bad* and *Badly* Badly

> TYRONE: Don't read that story; it's bad. Read this one about Harriet Tubman.
>
> HETA: Oh yes, I've heard about her. I want to read about her very badly.

Did you notice how Tyrone and Heta used *bad* and *badly* differently? Many people get confused over which of these words to use in a particular situation. In Tyrone's statement, he uses *bad* to modify the noun *story.* When Heta uses the word *badly,* she is modifying the verb *want.* If you can keep in mind whether you want to modify a noun or a verb, then you will not use *bad* and *badly* badly!

- Adjectives are words that modify nouns or pronouns. Because *bad* is an adjective, it should be used to modify *only* nouns or pronouns.

    > Tubman had a **bad** memory of the time the overseer hit her hard enough to leave a scar on her forehead. [*Bad* modifies the noun *memory.*]

    > The owner was a very **bad** man. [Here *bad* describes what type of *man* her owner was.]

NOTE: Be careful! The word *bad* should not be used to modify a verb.

> NONSTANDARD: Many masters treated the enslaved people bad.
>
> STANDARD: Many masters treated the enslaved people **badly.**

- *Badly* is an adverb and should be used to modify *only* a verb, an adjective, or another adverb.

    > The master punished the enslaved people when he thought that they had behaved **badly.** [*Badly* modifies the verb *behaved.*]

    > Many slaves wanted their freedom **badly.** [Here *badly* describes how much they wanted their freedom.]

A Special Case: *Feel*

The informal use of the expression "feel badly" has become acceptable, though it is not grammatically correct. In this usage, *feel* is a linking verb. A linking verb links the subject to a noun, pronoun, or adjective. An adverb never follows a linking verb.

> INFORMAL: Tubman felt badly about turning back.
>
> FORMAL: Tubman felt **bad** about turning back.

Using *bad* and *badly* correctly is exactly like using *good* and *well* correctly. First, decide what word you are modifying. Then you should know which form of the word to use—the adjective or the adverb.

EXERCISE A Identifying What Is Modified

Each of the following sentences uses the word *bad* or *badly.* Circle *bad* or *badly,* and draw an arrow pointing to the word that it modifies.

EXAMPLE: When Harriet behaved (badly,) Ben, her father, would punish her.

1. Tubman thought being sent to work on a chain gang was a bad situation.

2. Tubman wanted badly to help other slaves escape.

3. Some people thought that running away was a bad idea.

4. Tubman felt bad that she could not trust her husband.

5. Tubman's husband, John, thought badly of Tubman for running away from her master.

EXERCISE B Proofreading Paragraphs

The following paragraphs contain errors in the use of *bad* and *badly.* Cross out each error, and write the correct word above it. One mistake has been corrected for you. Find and correct five more mistakes.

After Tubman made her way to Pennsylvania, she still had much work to do. She wanted

badly
very ~~bad~~ to help other slaves achieve their freedom. However, she had to leave her husband

and brothers behind, and she missed them bad. When she remembered them, she often felt

badly about her decision. She also knew that if she had remained in the South, she would

have been separated from her husband and family as well. Owners often treated enslaved

families bad and separated family members from each other.

Tubman went to work for the Underground Railroad. She helped many people escape

slavery. Tubman hated slavery for many reasons. Not only were people often left in badly

physical condition, but they were also not treated like human beings. Tubman admired the

abolitionists, who believed that slavery was bad and worked to end it. In the end, Tubman

helped many slaves who wanted to escape bad. No doubt Tubman saved many lives in her

fight to free herself and others.

GRAMMAR LINK

The Fun They Had
Isaac Asimov   Pupil's Edition page 214

End All End-Mark Errors

> Margie hated the homework part the most she had to use a punch code

What's so confusing about the line above? It doesn't have any stop signs! It's really two separate sentences, but neither sentence has an **end mark.** Notice how much easier it is to read a sentence that has correct end marks. Also, notice that the first word of each sentence is capitalized.

> Margie hated the homework part the most**!** She had to use a punch code**.**

There are three different types of end marks: a period (.), a question mark (?), and an exclamation point (!). Read each sentence below aloud. Do you hear how the different end marks make each sentence sound different?

> Margie hated the homework part the most**.**
> Margie hated the homework part the most**?**
> Margie hated the homework part the most**!**

Below are some rules to follow when using end marks.

- Use a period at the end of a statement.

  > The inspector came to look at Margie's teacher**.**

- Use a question mark at the end of a question.

  > Why would anyone write a book about school**?**

- Use an exclamation point at the end of an exclamation.

  > Tommy thought he knew everything**!**

- Use a period or an exclamation point at the end of a request or command.

  > Please have a seat**.** [request]   Sit**!** [strong command]

EXERCISE A   Correcting Sentences by Adding End Marks

Make two sentences from each item below, adding end marks and capital letters where they are needed.

EXAMPLE: Tommy found a real book the words stood still on the page
> Tommy found a real book**!** The words stood still on the page.

1. Margie hated school she was doing worse and worse in geography

_____

2. Where did Tommy find the book he told Margie he found it in the attic

_____

_____

Elements of Literature   *Grammar and Language Link Worksheets* **21**

3. The inspector came to fix the teacher why didn't he just take the teacher away

_____

_____

4. How could a person be a teacher the person must be smart

_____

5. Kids went to school in a special building they could talk to each other

_____

_____

EXERCISE B **Proofreading Paragraphs for End Marks**

The following paragraphs are missing some important end punctuation. As you read the paragraphs, identify the spots where end marks are needed. Make the appropriate marks large and dark in the spot where they should be. Also, cross out any lowercase letter that should be capitalized, and write the capital letter above it. One missing end mark has been added as an example.

Margie was so excited**!** Tommy had found a real book. It seemed funny to hold a book in their hands they were used to reading books on a screen. Tommy had found the book in the attic. It was a very old book, with yellowed pages.

What did Tommy and Margie read about in the book they discovered that the book was about school. Margie couldn't understand why anyone would write about school. She hated school! It was so boring to sit alone in her room all day. The book said the teacher was a man. Margie's teacher was a machine.

The county inspector came to Margie's house to fix the mechanical teacher. He brought a box of tools and an apple for Margie he took the teacher apart. Margie was so disappointed when he fixed the teacher she was hoping he would take it away for a long time

What was school really like back then Margie imagined all the kids together. She sighed as she thought about it. What fun they must have had

GRAMMAR LINK

Zlateh the Goat
Isaac Bashevis Singer   Pupil's Edition page 249

Pronouns and Antecedents Always Agree

> Zlateh is a very special animal. She becomes a part of the family.

> No one would want to see his or her favorite animal hurt.

Pronouns take the place of nouns or of other pronouns. The noun or pronoun that a pronoun stands for is called its **antecedent.** Whenever you use a pronoun, you must be sure that the pronoun agrees in *number* (plural or singular) and in *gender* (male or female) with its antecedent.

Singular Personal Pronouns			
Gender	**Nominative Case**	**Objective Case**	**Possessive Case**
feminine	she	her	her, hers
masculine	he	him	his
neuter (neither)	it	it	its

> **Zlateh** is a female goat, and **she** gives milk. [The feminine pronoun *she* refers to the feminine antecedent, *Zlateh.*]

> **Aaron** might have starved, but Zlateh's milk saved **him.** [The masculine pronoun *him* refers to the masculine antecedent *Aaron.*]

> **It** kept **him** alive. [The neuter pronoun *it* refers to the milk. The masculine pronoun *him* refers to Aaron.]

- An **indefinite pronoun** refers to a person, place, or thing that is not specifically named. Use a singular pronoun to refer to the following indefinite pronouns:

anybody	anyone	each	either	everybody	someone
everyone	neither	nobody	no one	one	somebody

  EXAMPLE: **Each** of the men put on **his** coat.

- Use a plural pronoun to refer to the following indefinite pronouns:

  both   few   many   several

  EXAMPLE: **Both** Aaron and Zlateh enjoyed **their** time together.

NOTE: It can be impossible to determine what the gender of a pronoun should be when its antecedent is an indefinite pronoun. If the antecedent could refer to people of either gender, use both the masculine and feminine forms joined by *or.*

  EXAMPLE: No one in the family thought Aaron and Zlateh had survived. *Each* grieved in *his or her* own way.

NAME _____ CLASS _____ DATE _____

Using context clues, fill in the spaces provided with pronouns that agree with their antecedents in number and gender. The antecedents are the words in boldface type.

EXAMPLE: **Anyone** from the village can survive a blizzard if ___*he or she*___ knows how to find shelter.

1. **Aaron** stayed alive because _____ had Zlateh.

2. **Zlateh** gave _____ milk to Aaron.

3. **Each** village child knows that hay can keep _____ warm.

4. Zlateh ate the **hay.** _____ kept her nourished.

5. **One** of the girls in our class said that _____ used to have a goat.

6. Aaron hoped that if **someone** came by, _____ would be willing to help.

7. The **haystack** smelled good. _____ reminded Aaron of summer.

8. **Zlateh** felt safe as _____ slept near Aaron.

9. **Aaron** knew that Zlateh and the hay had kept _____ alive.

10. **Nobody** could take _____ goat to the butcher after an ordeal like Aaron's.

EXERCISE B Proofreading a Paragraph

In the paragraph below, cross out each word or word group in boldface type and write the correct pronoun above it. Then, draw an arrow from the pronoun to its antecedent. An example has been provided for you.

"Zlateh the Goat" is a wonderful story about a boy and ~~the boy's~~ *his* goat. At the beginning

of the story, Aaron, the boy, is told to sell Zlateh to the butcher. Aaron doesn't really want to,

but **Aaron** does not want to disobey **Aaron's** father. When Aaron and Zlateh set out for the

village on a sunny morning, Zlateh wonders where Aaron is taking **Zlateh.** However, Zlateh

trusts Aaron and allows **Aaron** to lead **Zlateh** along. When the weather turns stormy, the

two of them fear that **Aaron and Zlateh** are in danger. Luckily, Aaron finds shelter and food

for both of them. The two stay in **Zlateh and Aaron's** shelter for three days. Many of the

people in the town think Aaron is lost in the storm, and **many of the people in the town**

doubt he will survive. When Aaron and Zlateh return, the family members decide that **the**

family will never again consider selling **the family's** goat.

GRAMMAR LINK

Stray
Cynthia Rylant   **Pupil's Edition page 257**

Pronoun and Contraction Mix-ups

SON:	Whose turn is it to walk the dog?
DAUGHTER:	I think you're supposed to do it; I gave him a bath yesterday.
MOTHER:	I would just like to know who's going to walk the dog.
FATHER:	They're going to have to figure it out. Some chores should be theirs to decide.

Some of the handiest words in the English language are pronouns. By replacing nouns that have already been used, pronouns keep us from having to repeat them. However, one of the mistakes most often made in writing is confusing the possessive form of certain pronouns with a contraction. These commonly confused pronouns and contractions are listed below.

Possessive Form of Pronoun	Meaning	Contraction	Meaning
its	belonging to it	it's	it is, it has
their	belonging to them	they're	they are
your	belonging to you	you're	you are
whose	belonging to who	who's	who is, who has

INCORRECT:	Watch the puppy chase it's tail.
CORRECT:	Watch the puppy chase **its** tail.
INCORRECT:	Their going to be surprised when I bring the puppy home.
CORRECT:	**They're** going to be surprised when I bring the puppy home.
INCORRECT:	Do you think you're parents will let you keep it?
CORRECT:	Do you think **your** parents will let you keep it?
INCORRECT:	Mom will ask, "Whose going to take care of it?"
CORRECT:	Mom will ask, "**Who's** going to take care of it?"

Here is a method for deciding whether to use a contraction or a possessive pronoun. Whenever you are about to use either one, simply substitute the two words that form the contraction into your sentence. If your sentence still makes sense, you should use the contraction. If your sentence does not make sense, use the possessive pronoun form.

Watch the puppy chase *it is* tail. (*It is* does not make sense. Use the pronoun *its.*)

They are going to be surprised when I bring the puppy home. (*They are* makes sense. Use the contraction *they're.*)

Do you think *you are* parents will let you keep it? (*You are* does not make sense. Use the pronoun *your.*)

Mom will ask, "*Who is* going to take care of it?" (*Who is* makes sense. Use the contraction *who's*.)

EXERCISE A Choosing Between Pronouns and Contractions

For each sentence below, circle the correct word in parentheses.

EXAMPLE: The puppy opened (*it's*, (*its*)) sleepy eyes.

1. Doris, (*whose, who's*) supposed to care for the dog, went to get the dog food.

2. "Doris, be sure to feed (*your, you're*) dog," called Mr. Lacey.

3. The puppy wagged (*its, it's*) tail when Doris threw the ball.

4. "(*Its, It's*) nice to see her so happy," agreed the parents.

5. "(*Your, You're*) going to have to give the puppy a bath," Mr. Lacey said.

6. "(*Whose, Who's*) cute puppy is this?" asked the veterinarian.

7. When (*their, they're*) six months old, puppies need a rabies shot.

8. Dr. Vanwinkle, (*whose, who's*) the veterinarian, gave the puppy a treat.

9. The puppy received (*its, it's*) own special bedding.

10. Many people have changed (*their, they're*) minds about leaving animals at the pound.

EXERCISE B Proofreading a Paragraph

The following paragraph contains errors in the spelling and use of possessive pronouns and contractions. As you identify each error, cross it out and write the correct contraction or pronoun above it. One error has been identified and corrected as an example. Find five more.

It's
~~Its~~ delightful to see the special relationship that exists between a child and a dog. The

child, whose youthful energy knows no bounds, has a constant and loyal companion. Their

always together—on walks, watching TV, even sleeping at night. Parents, who's concerns are

mostly practical, often have to remind children to care for their dogs. Its there duty to say

things like "Feed you're dog." Although the parents may have to provide such reminders

often, their hearts are warmed to see child and pet happily at play.

GRAMMAR LINK

The Flood
Ralph Helfer
Pupil's Edition page 278

Clear Pronoun References

> Frank waded out into the raging river. Ralph held on to the end of a rope around Frank's waist. When he pulled on the rope, disaster threatened. Frank almost drowned as his friend watched in horror.

Pronouns are useful because they can take the place of nouns. They keep us from having to repeat the same nouns. However, pronouns also can cause confusion. In the paragraph above, which of the two men pulled on the rope? The word *he* could refer to either one of them.

A pronoun must have a clear **antecedent**—the noun or pronoun to which the pronoun refers. To refer to the antecedent more clearly, the author of the paragraph above should have said

> Frank waded out into the raging river. Ralph held on to the end of a rope around Frank's waist. When Ralph pulled on the rope, disaster threatened. Frank almost drowned as his friend watched in horror.

Now you can tell which man pulled on the rope.

In unclear pronoun references, a pronoun may refer to either of two antecedents, or the pronoun may not clearly refer to any antecedent.

UNCLEAR:	Ralph saw Ben. His eyes filled with tears. [Whose eyes filled with tears?]
CLEAR:	Ralph saw Ben. Ralph's eyes filled with tears.
UNCLEAR:	Los Angeles is more than two dozen miles south of Soledad Canyon. A stream cuts right through it. [Through which area does the stream cut?]
CLEAR:	Los Angeles is more than two dozen miles south of Soledad Canyon. A stream cuts right through the canyon.
UNCLEAR:	Toni looked at Sheba. She was excited but relieved. [Who was excited but relieved?]
CLEAR:	Toni looked at Sheba. Sheba was excited but relieved.
UNCLEAR:	Three girls saved the snakes. They were on the cowcatcher. [Who or what was on the cowcatcher?]
CLEAR:	Three girls saved the snakes. The girls were on the cowcatcher.

EXERCISE A   Identifying Clear and Unclear Sentences

Identify the following sentences as clear or unclear. For each of the unclear sentences, list the possible antecedents of the pronoun in boldface.

> **EXAMPLE:**   Ralph saw Bullfrog in the water. **He** could not get up the bank.
>
> _unclear, Ralph or Bullfrog_

1. A flood threatened the ranch and the hundreds of animals on **it.**

_____

2. When Frank Lamping and Ralph met, **he** spoke of the weakening dam.

_____

3. The trainers tried to rescue the fear-trained animals, but **they** did not trust them.

_____

4. They tried to save the animal in the cage. **It** was almost covered with water.

_____

5. A woman had brought coffee and ham to the workers, and **they** were grateful.

_____

EXERCISE B   Writing Clear Sentences

Rewrite the following sentences to make them contain clear pronoun references.

1. Bob had taken Clarence to the raging stream. He dared not jump across.

_____

_____

2. Ralph was fumbling with the key to the cage, but it fell into the water.

_____

_____

3. Toni and Ralph saw a lion and other animals on the top of a hill. They did not run away.

_____

_____

4. Miguel and Ralph talked. He was using some English words and some Spanish words.

_____

_____

5. Did Toni see Modoc when she was pulling the cages out of the water?

_____

_____

GRAMMAR LINK

from The Land I Lost
Huynh Quang Nhuong

Object Pronouns

After Trung realized that the moving tree was Lan, he rescued Lan.

Trung's mother liked the cookies that Lan brought Trung's mother.

Because the crocodile was so sneaky, Lan was surprised by the crocodile.

What's wrong with the sentences above? In each sentence, a word or phrase is repeated unnecessarily. **Object pronouns** can keep us from having to repeat words.

The object pronouns are *me, you, him, her, it, us,* and *them.* Use them as follows.

Object Pronoun Uses	How They Are Used	Example Sentence
Direct Objects	A **direct object** follows an action verb and tells whom or what received the action.	Trung rescued **her.**
Indirect Objects	An **indirect object** comes between an action verb and a direct object and tells to whom or to what (or for whom or for what) something is done.	Lan brought **her** cookies.
Objects of Prepositions	A **prepositional phrase** includes a preposition, a noun or pronoun called the **object of the preposition,** and any modifiers of that object.	Trung rowed the boat toward **her.**

EXERCISE A   Identifying Object Pronouns

Read each of the following sentences, and decide whether the italicized pronoun is a direct object, an indirect object, or an object of a preposition. Then, on the line provided, write **DO** for direct object, **IO** for indirect object, or **OP** for object of a preposition.

EXAMPLE: ___DO___ The crocodile was approaching *her.*

_____ **1.** Trung impressed his future mother-in-law when he gave *her* gifts.

_____ **2.** The crocodile traumatized *her.*

_____ **3.** The river was dangerous, so Trung took a boat across *it.*

_____ **4.** Hearing Trung's story scared *them.*

_____ **5.** Lan was above *him* in a tree.

EXERCISE B **Choosing the Right Pronoun**

Each sentence below has two pronouns in parentheses. Decide which pronoun is correct and circle it.

EXAMPLE: The wedding guests gave (*they,* (*them*)) gifts.

1. The crocodile attack was surprising to Trung and (*she, her*).

2. Behind (*her, she*) loomed the crocodile.

3. Trung's report that Lan had not returned worried the family and (*he, him*).

4. Trung wanted to shout at the crocodile, "Don't take our future away from Lan and (*I, me*)!"

5. The author presented an interesting story to (*us, we*).

EXERCISE C **Proofreading a Paragraph**

The following paragraph contains nouns that need to be changed to object pronouns. As you identify each of the nouns, cross it out and write the appropriate pronoun above it. One has been identified and corrected as an example. Find and correct five more.

After many long years, Trung and Lan are finally to be married. They happily prepare for

the day. To welcome Lan, Trung's family holds a dinner for ~~Lan~~. *(her)* The wedding is beautiful.

Trung and Lan are very much in love, and their mothers are happy for Trung and Lan. Later,

tragedy strikes. While Lan is bathing in the river, a wily old crocodile attacks Lan. When Lan

does not return from the river, Trung worries about Lan. It seems as if she and Trung will

have to say goodbye to happiness. Fortunately, she outwits the crocodile and is able to

escape from the crocodile. Lan signals to Trung, and she is reunited with Trung.

LANGUAGE LINK

from **All I Really Need to Know I Learned in Kindergarten**
Robert Fulghum   Pupil's Edition page 298

Style: Exaggeration Can Be Funny

> "She turns, sees me, gives me the big, smiling Hello, and takes three steps
> across her front porch. And goes, 'AAAAAAAAGGGGGGGGGGGHHHHHHHHHH!!!!'
> *(That's a direct quote.)* At about the level of a fire engine at full cry."

It would be spectacular if a human being could make a sound at "the level of a fire engine
at full cry." We might all have to wear earplugs! In reality, however, this comparison is a
humorous use of exaggeration. **Exaggeration** is a deliberate overstatement, often used to
create a humorous effect. Authors who use exaggeration make situations and characters
appear more extreme than they actually are.

EXERCISE A **Identifying Exaggeration**

Read each excerpt from *All I Really Need to Know I Learned in Kindergarten.* Answer the
questions that follow by writing the letter of the correct choice on the line provided.

_____ 1. "Tries opening the front door without unlocking it. Tries again. Breaks key in
the lock. Runs around the house headed for the back door. Doppler effect of
"AAAAAGGGHHHHaaggh . . ."

What is exaggerated most in this excerpt?

a. the difficulty she has opening the door
b. the trouble she has with the lock
c. the level of the sound she makes

_____ 2. "She has walked full force into a spider web. And the pressing question, of
course: Just where is the spider *now*? She flings her baggage in all directions.
And at the same time does a high-kick, jitterbug sort of dance . . ."

What is exaggerated most in this excerpt?

a. the importance of the location of the spider
b. the movement she makes
c. the force with which she walks into the web

_____ 3. "Clutches at her face and hair and goes 'AAAAAAAGGGGGGGGHHHHHHHH-
HH!!!!!' at a new level of intensity."

What is exaggerated most in this excerpt?

a. the fact that she makes a sound
b. the level of the sound she makes
c. the fact that the sound she makes is not an actual word

EXERCISE B **Identifying the Meanings of Exaggerations**

Below are some common expressions that are also exaggerations. On the line provided, write the real meaning of each exaggeration.

EXAMPLE: I have a million things to do.   I have a large number of things to do.

1. He's faster than a speeding bullet.   _____

2. I'm so hungry that I could eat a horse.   _____

3. She's as tall as a mountain.   _____

4. It's hotter than an oven outside.   _____

5. You look like a million dollars!   _____

EXERCISE C **Using Exaggerations**

Rewrite the following sentences by adding exaggerations to make them humorous.

EXAMPLE: The man swatted at the bee.

Flapping his hands at the speed of light, the man swatted at the bee.

1. The bee flew away.

_____

_____

2. Her house is old.

_____

_____

3. She thought the bee was huge.

_____

_____

4. Her stereo is very loud.

_____

_____

5. He is a very fast runner.

_____

_____

LANGUAGE LINK

All Summer in a Day
Ray Bradbury   **Pupil's Edition page 325**

Style: Figurative Language

> **JORGE:** Did you hear Margot's poem about the sun? I don't believe it.
>
> **MAYA:** How do you know? You've never seen the sun yourself. I saw a picture of a sunset on earth, and it was like an eye made of fire. It made the whole sky burn like explosives.
>
> **JORGE:** An eye of fire that made the sky explode? I can't figure you out! You talk as if you're from Mars.

Whether or not we are aware of it, **figurative language** forms a large part of our conversation. Although Jorge may think his friend Maya's description of the sun is unusual, he uses imaginative language himself when he says, "You talk as if you're from Mars." The expression is figurative, because it is a comparison that isn't literally true. Maya is not really from Mars, nor is the sun an eye of fire. Writers like Ray Bradbury use unusual comparisons—figurative language—to make their descriptions lively and vivid for the reader. There are many different kinds of figurative language. The most common are the *simile,* the *metaphor,* and *personification.*

A **simile** is a comparison between two unlike things, using a word such as *like, as, resembles,* or *than.*

> Her greeting was like a warm summer day.

A **metaphor** is a comparison between two unlike things in which one thing is described as another thing. The comparison is made without using a word such as *like, as, resembles,* or *than.*

> The sky is a bowl.

Personification is a way of describing a thing or a nonhuman part of nature as if it were human.

> The giant trees sighed when the sun appeared.

EXERCISE A Identifying Figurative Language

Underline the figurative expression in each sentence. Then, decide whether it is a simile, a metaphor, or personification. On the line before each sentence, write the letter **S** for simile, **M** for metaphor, or **P** for personification.

> **EXAMPLE:** ____S____ Tameka thought the landscape of Venus was <u>like a pressure cooker</u>, its dense atmosphere trapping heat and moisture.

_____ **1.** When she reads a science-fiction story, she feels as if she is being taken to visit another universe, where the familiar rules of gravity, motion, and time are altered.

_____ **2.** Geoffrey was amazed to sense the sun's warm hand, stroking his face with its

kind, gentle beams.

_____ **3.** Margot became a wilted flower as she sat locked in the closet.

_____ **4.** When the rain began to fall, the children's hearts sank, and they saw the bleak,

gray clouds glaring at them in the sky.

_____ **5.** "You're just like monsters," the teacher scolded. "Ganging up on Margot that

way was a terrible thing to do."

EXERCISE B **Completing Figurative Language**

Personification can add power or emotion to descriptive sentences. Complete each of the
following statements, creating your own personification to express something about each
subject.

EXAMPLE: The computer screen _____*sneered*_____ at Richard like a _____*mocking bully*_____

_*with flashing eyes*_____ .

1. Margot pressed her hands against the locked closet door; it _____

_____ .

2. With the sun's rays warming the jungle, the sun looked _____

_____ to the children of Venus.

3. My sister has never known any place except this colony on Venus. To me this planet is

like a wet, lifeless rag, but to her it's a _____ .

4. The ocean was so mysterious and lovely that it _____

_____ .

5. Jamal watered the dry rosebush, and when he was finished, the bush _____

_____ .

EXERCISE C **Using Figurative Language**

You arrive on Venus for a visit for the first time. On a separate sheet of paper, write a
paragraph describing what it is like. Use at least five figures of speech, including
metaphors, similes, and personification. Underline all figures of speech you use.

GRAMMAR LINK

Eleven / Once
Sandra Cisneros

Pupil's Edition page 336

Punctuating Dialogue

> KEVIN: Rosa said that sweater's not mine.
>
> DEANNA: Are you sure that's what she said?
>
> KEVIN: Actually, she said, "The sweater's not mine. It belongs to Josey."

Kevin's explanation to Deanna only begins to make sense when it is punctuated correctly; otherwise, it sounds as if Rosa meant that the sweater didn't belong to Kevin. When you are writing a story or essay with dialogue, using quotation marks correctly can save your reader confusion. Here are some rules for punctuating dialogue.

Rules	Examples
1. Put quotation marks around direct quotations of words spoken aloud.	"Do you really feel different when you turn thirteen?" Rosa asked her cousin Marta.
2. Begin a quoted remark with a capital letter.	In the confusion after recess, it was difficult for anyone to hear Rosa say, "The sweater is not mine."
3. Use a comma, a question mark, or an exclamation point (never a period) to separate a quotation from the speaker tag (the expression that identifies the speaker).	"I didn't feel like celebrating when I turned eleven," Rosa said. "Why not?" asked Marta. "Because I felt terrible!" Rosa exclaimed.
4. When the speaker tag interrupts a quoted sentence, the second part of the quotation begins with a lowercase letter.	"Put on the sweater right now," said the teacher, "or else I will put it on for you!"

EXERCISE A **Identifying Correct Punctuation in Dialogue**

Each of the following pairs of sentences could have been spoken by characters in "Eleven / Once." Circle the letter of the sentence that has correct punctuation and capitalization.

1. **a.** "Someone lost a sweater," Joey said as he picked up the sweater he had found.

   b. "Someone lost a sweater." Joey said as he picked up the sweater he had found.

2. **a.** Mrs. Price said, I will not tolerate any more laughter in this classroom!

   b. Mrs. Price said, "I will not tolerate any more laughter in this classroom!"

3. **a.** Rachel wished she had said, "It's not mine!"

   b. Rachel wished she had said it's not mine!

4. a. "I didn't remember until now," said Phyllis, "but the sweater belongs to me."

   b. "I didn't remember until now," said Phyllis, "But the sweater belongs to me."

5. a. Rachel confessed, "It was as if I were frozen and couldn't speak."

   b. Rachel confessed, "it was as if I were frozen and couldn't speak."

EXERCISE B **Proofreading Paragraphs**

The following paragraphs contain errors in the use of capitalization, quotation marks, and other punctuation. As you identify errors in capitalization, cross out each incorrect letter and write the correct form above it. When you find missing quotation marks or other missing punctuation marks, make each mark in the appropriate place and circle it. Three errors have been corrected. Find and correct ten more.

Rachel used to look forward to her upcoming birthdays. When she turned eight, she

couldn't wait. "it's so much fun to have a party and a big cake she told her cousin Marta.

Actually, when she thinks about it now, many of her birthdays have been letdowns, disap-

pointing days when she felt as though she were a punctured tire with the air leaking out.

She called Marta and asked, "does it feel different when you become a teenager? Marta

was two years older, and she seemed to know everything. Rachel thought it was a shame

that she couldn't catch up with her cousin. When Marta was eleven, Rachel was only nine.

Now that Rachel was finally becoming eleven herself, Marta was still ahead of her, of course.

Thirteen and proud of it!

Rachel asked her, "is it fun to be thirteen?

"Well, Marta replied, it's not bad. You get to do some things you couldn't do as a child."

Like what? asked Rachel.

Having a job, for one thing! Marta said. "I spent all last weekend baby-sitting!"

LANGUAGE LINK

The Gold Cadillac
Mildred D. Taylor

Style: Connotations

CADILLAC SALESPERSON:	This car is the *king* of the road. It's the *top banana,* the real thing, a one-hundred percent guarantee of *luxury, luxury,* and more *luxury*. It's *solid gold* from bumper to tailpipe, a *jewel* of a car, a *priceless chariot* fit for a *prince.*
CUSTOMER:	Just how much would a prince have to pay for this "priceless chariot"?

Connotations are the feelings and associations that words suggest. The Cadillac salesperson is well aware of the connotations of the words used to describe the car. In fact, the salesperson purposely loads the sales pitch with associations of royalty, elegance, and leisure to convince the customer that this is the most desirable car. Of course, the customer knows that it takes hard work and many paychecks to purchase a gold Cadillac! When the customer repeats the word "priceless," it has a different connotation for him, because he is being sarcastic.

Some words have positive connotations, while other words with similar meanings have entirely negative connotations. Think about the difference between the words *thrifty* and *cheap*. The first word implies a person who saves his or her money wisely; it has positive connotations. The second word also has to do with saving money, but the connotations are negative; a cheap person is stingy.

Using a thesaurus will sometimes be helpful if you are searching for an interesting synonym for an overused word. A thesaurus will provide a list of many words that have similar meanings, but it's up to you as a writer to search for the one that has the right connotation and feeling to express what you wish to say.

EXERCISE A   Changing Connotations

Each of the following sentences contains an underlined word. Decide whether the connotation of this word is positive or negative, and write the letter **P** (for positive) or **N** (for negative) on the line provided. Then, rewrite the original sentence, replacing the underlined word with a word or phrase of your own that has a similar meaning but the opposite connotation.

EXAMPLE: ___P___ All the neighbors were astonished to see our father drive up in such a fancy car.

All the neighbors were astonished to see our father drive up in such a gaudy car.

_____ **1.** 'Lois and her sister were surprised by their mother's firm refusal to ride in the Cadillac.

_____

_____

_____ **2.** 'Lois's mother thought it was <u>reckless</u> for her husband to buy an expensive car.

_____

_____

_____ **3.** After the Cadillac was sold, the family rode in a <u>classic</u> Ford.

_____

_____

_____ **4.** 'Lois thought her ride through the South in the <u>splendid</u> Cadillac would remain a memory forever.

_____

_____

_____ **5.** The signs that 'Lois saw in the windows of restaurants and motels made her <u>curious</u>.

_____

_____

EXERCISE B **Comparing Connotations**

For each pair of sentences below, put a plus sign (+) in the space next to the sentence containing the underlined word or phrase with stronger connotations. Place a minus sign (−) next to the sentence containing the underlined word or phrase with the weaker connotations.

EXAMPLE: ___+___ Len was a <u>lightning</u> runner.

___−___ Len was a <u>fast</u> runner.

_____ **1.** The Cadillac looked <u>brilliant</u> in the sunlight.

_____ The Cadillac looked <u>shiny</u> in the sunlight.

_____ **2.** I saw my father look <u>enraged</u>.

_____ I saw my father look <u>angry</u>.

_____ **3.** 'Lois was <u>happy</u> the neighbors could see her family's new car.

_____ 'Lois was <u>delighted</u> the neighbors could see her family's new car.

_____ **4.** The old Ford <u>moved at a leisurely pace</u>.

_____ The old Ford <u>inched along sluggishly</u>.

_____ **5.** The policeman was <u>brutally unjust</u>.

_____ The policeman was <u>unreasonable</u>.

GRAMMAR LINK

The Bracelet
Yoshiko Uchida
Pupil's Edition page 365

Look Who's Talking

> When Alma got home, her mother asked her, "Where were you? I looked all over the house, and I couldn't find you anywhere."
>
> "I went to say goodbye to Suki and her family. I don't understand why they can't stay in their home like everyone else."
>
> Her mother looked at her sadly. "It's hard to say goodbye to a friend, especially when you don't know where she's going, or what lies ahead."

In the dialogue above, we can tell when Alma is speaking and when her mother is responding, even though there is no speaker tag to tell us "Alma said" or "her mother answered." We know because the writer introduces each new quotation by beginning a new paragraph. Each paragraph break indicates that another person is speaking.

When you write dialogue (a conversation), begin a new paragraph each time the speaker changes.

EXAMPLE: "Did you look to see if the bracelet fell into your sleeve? That happened to me once when I thought I'd lost a bracelet," said Yoko.
   "Yes," said Suki sadly. "I couldn't find it anywhere."
   "Never mind," said Mama. "You'll remember Alma anyway, even without the bracelet."

NOTE: Sometimes dialogue paragraphs may be only one line long.

What should you do if one speaker is repeating someone else's words within a quotation? When you write a nested quotation—that is, a quotation within a quotation—use single quotation marks to enclose one quotation within the other.

EXAMPLES: Nguyen said, "At school today Mrs. Ramos said to the class, 'As a holiday gift, you will all get a week without homework.'"

   "That's funny," Lamar replied. "I heard that Mrs. Ramos said, 'As a holiday gift, you will all get a *day* without homework.'"

EXERCISE A   Punctuating Nested Quotations

Correct each sentence below by adding and circling single quotation marks to punctuate the nested quotation. If there is no nested quotation, write **C** after the sentence.

EXAMPLE: "I heard Zachary say, 'I'll be out for dinner as soon as my homework is done,'" said Dad.

1. "Yolanda told me that she heard Mr. Méndez say, Your book reports are due on Friday."

2. "The sportscaster on the news said, The game has been canceled on account of bad weather," said Sal.

3. "I heard Geraldo say that he was not coming to the party," reported Linda.

4. "The doctor said, It's a healthy baby girl!" shouted Eli as he entered the waiting room.

5. "When we arrived at the museum, Mrs. Govea said, Enjoy the tour, but stay together," said Miki, reminding us of our instructions.

EXERCISE B Proofreading Paragraphs

The following paragraphs involve a conversation that could have taken place between Ruri, Laurie, Keiko, and Ruri's mother. The paragraphs contain errors in the use of quotation marks and in paragraph breaks. As you identify errors, put quotation marks where they are needed and circle them. When a new person is speaking, make a symbol ¶ to show where the new paragraph should begin. One of each type of error has been identified and corrected as an example.

Nancy said, Thomas and I were wondering where Keiko and Ruri live now." "I don't know,

Laurie replied, "but I really miss my best friend. I wonder if Ruri is thinking about me, too."

Mama had done wonders in making the little stall seem more like home. "Look at the

way she's brightened up the place!" Keiko declared. "I think it looks very nice," Ruri replied.

"Still, I miss our real home."

"I know it's difficult for you children," said Mama, but at least we have each other.

"That's true," said Keiko. Ruri was still silent. "What's the matter, honey?" asked Mama. You

still look very sad; maybe you should tell us what's wrong.

Ruri murmured, "I wish I could cry, but I feel too scared and numb. I wanted to keep my

promise to Laurie about the bracelet. I said I wasn't ever going to take the bracelet off, so I

could look at it and keep her with me." "She is with you, in your heart," Mama explained, "just

as your father and I are joined together, even though we can't see each other. Remembering

someone you care for is the most important thing."

GRAMMAR LINK

What Do Fish Have to Do with Anything?

Avi   **Pupil's Edition page 378**

Direct and Indirect Quotations

> Willie wondered whether fish who live in caves feel unhappy. He asked his mother, "Do you think human beings are the only ones who feel sad sometimes, or do other animals have emotions, too?"
>
> "I don't know," his mother replied, in her most frustrated tone of voice.
>
> She said that he should stop wondering about questions that no one could answer. His mother told him he should eat his cake and then go do his homework.

In the passage above, you will notice both **direct quotations**—a person's exact words—and **indirect quotations**—paraphrases, or rewordings, of direct quotations. Use quotation marks to enclose only a direct quotation, not an indirect quotation.

DIRECT: "I don't know," his mother replied.

INDIRECT: His mother said that she didn't know.

When a quotation consists of several sentences, place quotation marks at the beginning and at the end of the whole quotation.

EXAMPLE: "Sometimes people walk around without an umbrella when it's pouring outside. If you have an extra umbrella, it's up to you to share it. How else are we going to be friends?" said the homeless man.

EXERCISE A   Punctuating Quotations

Determine whether each of the following sentences is a direct or an indirect quotation. If it is a direct quotation, rewrite it on the line provided, adding quotation marks where they are needed. If it is an indirect quotation, write **I**.

EXAMPLE: Why not, Mom? Willie demanded.

"Why not, Mom?" Willie demanded. _____

1. Willie's teacher told the class about fish that have no eyes.

   _____

   _____

2. Mrs. Markham asked, Willie, have you seen a movie about fish or something?

   _____

   _____

3. Willie replied, I've seen the movie *Free Willy,* but it's about a whale, not a fish.

_____

_____

4. Mrs. Markham told Willie that she thought money would cure most people's unhappiness.

_____

_____

5. Willie said, I'd rather have a whale be my friend than have a whole big bag full of money.

_____

_____

EXERCISE B **Paraphrasing Direct Quotations**

On the line provided, change each direct quotation to an indirect quotation. Change words and punctuation marks as necessary.

> **EXAMPLE:** "Do you want to eat a slice of poundcake?" asked Willie's mother.
> Willie's mother asked him whether or not he wanted to eat a slice of poundcake.

1. "People always need a little extra," the man explained to Willie.

_____

_____

2. Caroline said, "I felt disappointed when I discovered that adults don't have all the answers, either."

_____

_____

3. Willie said, "It's hard when they tell you not to ask questions."

_____

_____

4. Mrs. Markham remarked, "I came to pick up my son because I feel parents must protect their children."

_____

_____

5. Tina asked Willie, "Have you seen that man who used to beg on our street? I wonder where he's gone."

_____

_____

GRAMMAR LINK

Loo-Wit, the Fire-Keeper
retold by Joseph Bruchac

Pupil's Edition page 497

Forming the Plurals of Nouns

FOR SALE

Prime piece of property complete with the following:

- not one house but three hice, hand built of stone
- four pair of oxes, strong and ready to work
- a flock of wild gooses
- herds of cattle, sheeps, and goat's
- two vallies and many mountaines

A great deal! Owner hoping to move to the other side of the fence.

Although the maker of this sign may know how to make the property sound attractive, he or she doesn't know how to change the singular forms of nouns into their plural forms. Forming plurals isn't difficult once you learn the rules. Most plural nouns follow these rules, although there are some nouns with irregular plural forms. A dictionary is helpful for checking the correct spelling of irregular plural forms.

Types of Nouns	What to Do	Examples
Most singular nouns	Add –s	kittens, brothers, creators, lungs
Nouns ending in s, x, z, ch, or sh	Add –es	gases, boxes, waltzes, inches, wishes
Nouns ending in a *vowel* plus o	Add –s	stereos, rodeos, radios, patios, igloos
Nouns ending in a *consonant* plus y	Change the y to i and add –es	puppy/puppies, candy/candies, city/cities, army/armies
Nouns ending in a *vowel* plus y	Add –s	holiday/holidays, bay/bays, decoy/decoys

NAME _____ CLASS _____ DATE _____

Some nouns don't fit the rules.

Types of Nouns	What to do	Examples
Nouns ending in a *consonant* plus *o*	• Add -*es* • Add -*s or* -*es*	• toma**toes**, pota**toes**, ech**oes**, her**oes** • mosqui**tos** or mosqui**toes**, ban**jos** or ban**joes**
Nouns ending in *f* or *fe*	• Add -*s* • Change *f* or *fe* to *v* and add -*es*	• belief/belief**s**, giraffe/giraffe**s** • knife/kni**ves**, thief/thie**ves**
Some singular nouns	Use a new word for the plural	ox/oxen, woman/women, tooth/teeth, foot/feet, goose/geese
Some singular nouns	Use the same form for singular and plural	sheep, deer

EXERCISE A Spelling the Plurals of Nouns

On the line provided, spell the plural form of each of the following nouns.

1. fox _____
2. loaf _____
3. cheese _____
4. monkey _____
5. tax _____
6. patio _____
7. man _____
8. toy _____
9. mouse _____
10. puppy _____
11. gulf _____
12. rash _____
13. piano _____
14. moose _____
15. strawberry _____

EXERCISE B Writing with Plurals

Write a paragraph about "Loo-Wit, the Fire-Keeper." Change the following singular nouns to plural nouns and include them in your paragraph.

brother   people   chief   life   sky

_____
_____
_____
_____
_____
_____

LANGUAGE LINK

from Volcano
Patricia Lauber

Pupil's Edition page 511

Style: Comparisons in Science Writing

(FROM A NEWSCAST)   After a long period of inactivity, Mount St. Helens has erupted in an explosion of anger.

In the description of volcanic activity, the newscaster uses the language of human emotion to convey a sense of the natural drama. We often use **figures of speech** as imaginative ways of comparing unlike things. One common figure of speech is called **personification;** it is a way of describing an object as if it possessed human qualities. Sometimes we give human feelings and qualities to our pets, to the weather, and to technology. Objects in our lives become almost human through the use of figures of speech. In writing, **personification** may make a description lively and compelling, giving something nonhuman the abilities and personality of a living person.

EXAMPLE: The smoke from the volcanic explosion **crept around the corner and pinched my nose** with its burning odor.

EXERCISE A   Identifying Personification

Carefully read each of the following sentences. In each sentence, identify and underline each use of personification.

EXAMPLE: The clouds wept at the sight of the charred forest.

1. The goldfish looked up at me with sad, lonely eyes.

2. The extreme heat and the explosions of the volcano created flames that danced through the trees.

3. The mouth of the volcano yawned wide as it released a horrendous burst of gas and fire.

4. The tremendous winds angrily snatched my hat from my hand.

5. The sun smiled with comfort upon the surviving wildlife.

EXERCISE B   Finding the Figure of Speech

Read each of the following sentences. If you find an example of personification, underline it and write the letter **P** on the line provided. If the sentence has no example of personification, write **X** on the line.

EXAMPLE: __P__ Jamal saw the volcano hiding its head in the clouds.

_____ 1. Melissa wondered about the striking shape of the crater that formed at the top of Mount St. Helens. It was like a crescent moon.

_____ 2. The mudflows raced over the injured landscape.

_____ 3. The hot rock shattered, a glass mirror breaking into a million fragments.

_____ 4. Mount St. Helens stands head and shoulders above adjacent peaks in the Cascade Range.

_____ 5. When the eruptions stopped, scientists wondered whether the plant life would return, and whether nature would heal itself after its suffering.

EXERCISE C Writing Using Personification

Read each of the following descriptions of nature or scientific technology. Then, rewrite each sentence in the space provided, using personification to make the description more lively.

EXAMPLE: The computer broke down during the electrical storm, and I couldn't retrieve my files.

The computer suffered amnesia during the electrical storm and lost all

memory of my files.

1. Hot ash poured from the volcano's peak and covered the town.

_____

_____

_____

2. Lancelot discovered that the computer was malfunctioning again.

_____

_____

_____

3. On the news, we saw some photographs taken from inside a deep volcanic crater.

_____

_____

_____

4. Hot magma boils inside the earth's crust.

_____

_____

_____

5. Nora searched for a pair of pliers, but she could not imagine where they were.

_____

_____

_____

GRAMMAR LINK

The Seventh Sister
retold by Cindy Chang   **Pupil's Edition page 536**

Using Commas to Separate Adjectives in a Series

MANDY: Today in school we learned a Chinese legend—that the Milky Way comes from the sad, lonely tears of a woman named Mei who used to cry as she wove her tapestry of the night.

MOM: Oh dear, she must have spent eons in tears.

When Mandy tells her mother about Mei's sadness, she uses several different descriptive words, or adjectives, to tell her impression of the story. Commas separate two or more adjectives before a noun. They make it clear to the reader that a series of adjectives is modifying the same noun.

EXAMPLE: The starry**,** mysterious**,** dark sky is full of galaxies we do not know.

Do not put a comma between an adjective and a noun immediately following it.

INCORRECT: Mei and her sisters were skillful, deft, weavers.

CORRECT: Mei and her sisters were skillful**,** deft weavers.

If the final adjective in a series is closely related in meaning to the noun, do not use a comma before that adjective. To decide whether or not a comma is needed, add the word *and* between the adjectives, then read the sentence back to yourself. If the *and* sounds strange, as in the example below, you shouldn't use a comma.

INCORRECT: Mei made colorful, silk tapestries.

INCORRECT: Mei made colorful *and* silk tapestries.

CORRECT: Mei made colorful silk tapestries.

EXERCISE A   Placing Commas in Sentences

Rewrite the following sentences on the lines provided, adding commas where they are necessary and removing any that do not belong. If the sentence is correct as it is, write **C** on the line.

EXAMPLE: Mei missed her sisters, but she soon grew accustomed to the joyful**,** melodious harmony of life with Chang on earth.

1. I think there is nothing so lovely as the sight of a pair of bright glowing stars in the sky.

_____

_____

2. When can we hear the story about Chang's sweet sorrowful love songs?

_____

_____

3. Chang goes to find a single magpie feather.

_____

_____

4. He approaches the silver reflecting pond, and he sees the enchanted shimmering magpie feather he wants.

_____

_____

5. Mei cries sorrowfully when she realizes she must return to her sisters to relieve the tired, angry sun.

_____

_____

EXERCISE B **Proofreading Paragraphs**

The following paragraphs contain errors in the use of commas. Add missing commas, and use an X to cross out each unnecessary comma. One error has been identified and corrected as an example. Find and correct ten more.

People from many different cultures have told stories about the stars in the sky, yet nobody has ever explained their origin completely. The mythological stories of the ancient Greeks are full of vengeful irresponsible, gods and goddesses. Many of these gods and goddesses place their monsters or favorite heroes in the starry sky. One such hero is the strong valiant ill-treated Hercules. Hercules suffered from the jealousy of devious sly Hera, who was queen of all the gods.

The Chinese myth of the Seventh Sister gives an endearing explanation. Chang and Mei are placed in the sky to preserve their enduring, love. They are allowed to be united once a year. At all other times Mei must be occupied with her beautiful, tapestry making. Chang and Mei are a pair of glorious brilliant stars, yet they are separated most of the year by a galaxy called the Milky Way. These patient tender sweethearts are as brave as the mighty, Hercules in their own way.

GRAMMAR LINK

Scanning the Heavens
George Beshore   **Pupil's Edition page 544**

Using Commas to Separate Items in a Series

Did you know that astronomers in ancient China had many theories about the earth's shape, size, location, and origin? Some believed the universe was like a giant egg with the earth as its yolk.

It is important to use commas to separate ideas in a sentence. We can better understand the first sentence above because the commas indicate where to pause as we read.

EXAMPLE: I went to the library to read about science, philosophy, art, and religion in second-century China.

Series of items must be separated by commas. Commas help the reader to make sense of different items, phrases, or clauses in a series. They allow the reader to see where one item ends and a new one begins within a series.

• Use commas to separate words in a series. These words may be nouns, verbs, adverbs, or adjectives.

EXAMPLES: Chinese astronomers observed stars, planets, and the moon. *[nouns]*
Chinese astronomers awaited, observed, and recorded changes in the heavens. *[verbs]*
A nova is a guest star with a brief, dramatic, and brilliant career. *[adjectives]*

• Use commas to separate phrases in a series.

EXAMPLE: Observing planets, calculating lunar cycles, and recording data, ancient astronomers made great discoveries about the heavens.

• Use commas to separate clauses in a series.

EXAMPLES: During the last eclipse the sky darkened, the moon vanished, and an eerie light filled the streets. *[short independent clauses]*
The Chinese emperor Huang-Ti taught the people how to perform music, where to find silkworms, and how to use written symbols to record their thoughts. *[subordinate clauses]*

EXERCISE A   Using Commas in Sentences

For each of the following sentences, add and circle commas to separate items in a series. Remember to use commas to separate words, phrases, and clauses in a series.

EXAMPLE: Five hundred years before astronomers in the West, Chinese scientists could record, observe, and predict accurately when a lunar eclipse would occur.

1. Chinese astronomers measured the orbits of celestial bodies predicted natural events and recorded celestial phenomena.

2. Farmers philosophers priests and kings were all interested in learning about the stars.

3. The astronomers were able to predict changing seasons tidal conditions eclipses and other events on earth by studying the stars and planets.

4. Through an examination of their scientific practices writing skills calendars and records of the natural world, modern scholars have found evidence that the ancient Chinese were an advanced civilization.

5. How long ago did the emperor Huang-Ti teach the people to raise silkworms collect the silken fibers use a calligraphic system of writing and play music?

EXERCISE B **Proofreading Paragraphs**

Carefully proofread the following paragraphs. Add and circle commas where they are needed to separate items in a series. One correction has been made as an example. Find ten more.

Modern scientists were astounded when they began to examine the cultural, artistic

and astronomical knowledge of ancient Chinese civilization. Long before there were high-

powered telescopes weather satellites or other modern tools, Chinese astronomers were

able to calculate an accurate calendar by observing the heavens. They also understood that

orbits of celestial bodies could be monitored measured and understood by close observation.

When Marco Polo visited Beijing in the thirteenth century, he encountered a population of

avid knowledgeable stargazers.

Five hundred years before astronomers in the West, Chinese scientists began to predict

study and observe the appearance of lunar eclipses solar eclipses comets, and novas. Novas

were called guest stars; they lasted only two days, appearing bright at first, then rapidly

burning out and exploding just before disappearing from sight.

LANGUAGE LINK

How the Snake Got Poison
retold by Zora Neale Hurston　　　　　　　　　　**Pupil's Edition page 553**

Style: Dialect—The Voice of the People

> **PIGEON:**　Good mornin', Badger! What's shakin'?
>
> **BADGER:**　Just rocks rattlin' round in my noggin, I reckon.
>
> **PIGEON:**　Well, I could of speculated that much, I figure.

Pigeon and Badger understand each other, even though their vocabularies and accents may not be "standard." Although we hear a uniform way of speaking on television news programs, the language that we speak can be very different. Some of these differences in sentence structure, pronunciation, vocabulary, and expression relate to certain ethnic, social, and geographic groups. Others are particular to a school or business, or are shared by one's age group. Teens speak differently from their parents, just as New Yorkers often speak a dialect unlike the one spoken by Mississippians. **Dialect** is one name for a variety of spoken English. The informal and vivid ways in which different Americans express themselves offer rich material upon which writers like Zora Neale Hurston have drawn.

Some kinds of writing, such as a composition for class, business letter, or factual report, should be written in **formal English,** which obeys certain rules of grammar and usage. Other kinds of writing, such as fiction, poetry, or a personal letter, may reflect an individual's dialect, drawing on the energy of informal speech.

EXERCISE A　Identifying Informal Language

Some of the following sentences are written in slang or in dialect—informal English—while others are written in standard, formal language. Write **I** beside the sentences written in informal English—language you might use in a conversation or in a letter to a friend. Write **F** beside sentences written in a formal style—language you might use in an essay or report.

EXAMPLE:　____F____　I believe it is time for our evening meal.

　　　　　　　____I____　Let's get us some grub.

_____ **1.** Hajin, stop schmoozing and get it in gear.

_____ **2.** I don't want nothing to do with you and your kind, Lefty.

_____ **3.** The snake is a dangerous and deadly reptile.

_____ **4.** Jenna, you look down in the mouth this early mornin'.

_____ **5.** Zora Neale Hurston is one of our foremost African American storytellers.

EXERCISE B **Rewriting Dialogue**

Read the following conversation between Skunk and Snake. Then, on the lines provided, try to rewrite it in another dialect. You may "translate" some of the special expressions into something that sounds like an authentic local dialect from your community, or try it out in the elaborate, flowery English that characters might speak in a Shakespearean play. You might also try to re-create the "tough-guy" vocabulary from a gangster movie or detective show.

EXAMPLE: "Good afternoon, Snake, I wonder if I might have a word with you?"

"Howdy, Snake, wanna have a little parley-vous?"

1. SKUNK: "Afternoon, Snake. I wonder if I might obtain your advice."

_____

_____

2. SNAKE: "By all means, my good chap. You're looking dandy today, Sir Skunk. What's on your mind?"

_____

_____

3. SKUNK: "The problem, my good friend, is a certain conspicuous smell—not to mince words, a skunky odor I give off in the presence of others."

_____

_____

4. SNAKE: "Ah, I see, I see."

_____

_____

5. SKUNK: "It's got to be resolved. It's a terrible thing to smell like a skunk, a real social problem."

_____

_____

6. SNAKE: "And you would prefer to smell like—?"

_____

_____

7. SKUNK: "Like a rose, or a daffodil, or a wild strawberry blossom. This skunky scent just won't do. People see me, and all they say is 'pee-yew!'"

_____

_____

NAME _____ CLASS _____ DATE _____

Medusa's Head
retold by Olivia Coolidge

Pupil's Edition page 588

Style: Words from Myths

What's in a name? Plenty, if you happen to share a name with Pluto, Medusa, Mars, or some other Greek or Roman mythical figure. These names have entered our everyday language.

Name	Description from Myths	Modern Meaning
Pluto	the god of the underworld	the ninth planet; a Disney cartoon character
Medusa	the Gorgon with snakes for hair	a type of jellyfish
Mars	the Roman god of war	a planet; also the root word for *martial,* meaning "related to war"

EXERCISE A Identifying Mythic Figures

Match the names of these mythic characters with their descriptions. You may use a dictionary to help you.

Titans   Proteus   Atlas   Tantalus   Hercules

_____ 1. the mythic Greek king who was punished by being tempted with irresistible fruit and water that were moved out of his reach when he was hungry or thirsty

_____ 2. a race of gigantic Greek gods

_____ 3. the demigod who completed twelve impossible tasks

_____ 4. a Greek sea god capable of assuming different shapes

_____ 5. the strong Greek demigod who supported the heavens on his shoulders

EXERCISE B Understanding Modern Meanings

From the five Greek and Roman characters described above come the following words:

titanic   protean   atlas   tantalize   herculean

From what you know about the original story behind each character's name, see whether you can determine the modern meaning of each of these words. You can use a dictionary to help you. On the line provided, write the correct word for each definition.

_____ 1. huge or enormous

_____ 2. to tease by showing something but keeping it out of reach

_____ 3. requiring great power or force

_____ **4.** a collection of maps

_____ **5.** easily changing into different shapes or roles

EXERCISE C **Using Context Clues**

Read the sentences below. Using the context clues and what you know about the origins and meanings of the words below, complete each sentence with the correct word.

titanic	protean	atlas	tantalize	herculean

1. Myths are full of gods with _____ personalities. Sometimes the gods are kind; sometimes they are mean. People never know what to expect from many of the gods.

2. One trick of the gods is to _____ people. The gods promise great rewards but then give people tasks too difficult to complete. The reward is always just out of reach.

3. One main theme of myths is that a character must complete a(n) _____ task. The job usually demands great skill or power to complete.

4. Sometimes these characters have to travel to strange lands. It's amazing they can find their way without a(n) _____ to guide them.

5. In these strange lands they sometimes cross _____ mountains, which tower above them.

EXERCISE D **Creating New Words**

Using each name of a character from "Medusa's Head" below, create a new word and explain its meaning. One has been completed as an example.

	New Word / Part of Speech	The Meaning	The Reason for That Meaning
EXAMPLE: Danae	danous adjective	patient; courageous (from <u>Danae</u> + <u>ous</u>)	As the daughter of King Acrisios, Danae patiently endured much misery at the hands of her father.
Perseus			
Polydectes			
Gorgons			
Acrisios			

GRAMMAR LINK

Baucis and Philemon
retold by Olivia Coolidge   **Pupil's Edition page 597**

Homophones

There in a humble cottage, two strangers find hosts who serve their best
food and drink and let the strangers know that they're welcome.

What three words in the sentence above sound the same but have different spellings and
meanings? The words *there, their,* and *they're* are known as **homophones.** It's important
to know the differences in meaning between these words. Here are some guidelines to
help you with these and other homophones.

their	possessive form of *they*	**Their** cottage was small.
there	adverb used to mean "at that place" word used with a form of *to be* to start a sentence	The gods went **there** to seek hospitality. **There** was a kind welcome for them.
they're	contraction of *they are*	**They're** happy to find such a generous couple.
peace	noun meaning "quiet; order; security"	Philemon and Baucis lived together in **peace.**
piece	noun meaning "a part of something"	Philemon ate a **piece** of bacon.
weak	adjective meaning "feeble; not strong"	Philemon was too **weak** to catch the goose.
week	noun meaning "seven days"	They ate the food for a whole **week.**
your	possessive form of *you*	"**Your** meal is very generous," said Zeus.
you're	contraction of *you are*	"**You're** very kind," replied Philemon.

EXERCISE A   Choosing the Correct Word

In each of the following sentences, circle the word in parentheses that makes the sentence
correct.

EXAMPLE: On (there, *their*) way through the forest, Zeus and Hermes stopped.

1. (There, They're) in a little cottage lived an old couple.

2. (Their, They're) home was poor, but it was filled with (piece, peace).

3. They quickly gathered enough food to feed the guests for a (weak, week).

4. "(Your, You're) kindness will never be forgotten," the strangers promised.

5. (They're, Their) reward was to choose anything they wanted from the gods.

EXERCISE B   Proofreading Paragraphs

The following paragraphs contain errors in the use of homophones that are easily
confused. As you identify each error, cross out the word and write the correct word above
it. One error has been identified and corrected as an example. Find and correct ten more.

With no hotels or restaurants, hospitality was important to the Greeks. The custom was

for people to share ~~there~~ *their* homes and food with travelers. Of course, they're are different

ways to show hospitality. Some people would share only the best of what they had, treating

strangers like honored guests. Others might share only the bare necessities. Still others

might refuse to share at all. They might say, "We've got a sick relative here who is too week

to move. Take you're request to another house."

Baucis and Philemon would never refuse to help a stranger. Even though they were

poor, this couple was eager to help. When Zeus and Hermes knocked on their door, they

immediately began to treat they're guests generously. Only their best would do for these

guests. Instead of serving one peace of fruit, Baucis put out many different kinds. The gods

were deeply touched by their kindness.

"You're hospitality has not gone unnoticed," they said. They asked the elderly couple to

choose there reward. Philemon asked that they're cottage be transformed into a temple.

They wanted to continue to live in piece for the rest of their lives.

Philemon asked that they be allowed to die at the same time. There love was so strong that

they couldn't stand to be apart. So week after week, the two lived happily together. Finally,

when they became too weak to stand, the gods transformed them into two beautiful trees.

GRAMMAR LINK

Quetzalcoatl
retold by Amy Cruse

Pupil's Edition page 607

Effect vs. *Affect* and Other Words Often Confused

Which sentence below is correct?

How did the effect of the wine on Quetzalcoatl affect the lives of the Toltecs?

or

How did the affect of the wine on Quetzalcoatl effect the lives of the Toltecs?

If you chose the first sentence, you're right! If you weren't sure, you're not alone. It's easy to get confused about whether to use *effect* or *affect*. Below are some tips to help you use these words correctly.

• *Affect* is a verb that means "to influence."	• A wise ruler positively **affects** the lives of the people.
• *Effect* as a verb means "to accomplish" or "to bring about." • *Effect* as a noun means "the result of some action."	• Tezcatlipoca knew he had to **effect** a big change. • His evil trick had a bad **effect** on the whole country.

Affect and *effect* aren't the only words that are easy to confuse. Below are some others that can create problems if you're not careful.

• *desert* (dez′ərt) — a noun that means "a dry, sandy region" • *desert* (di•zʉrt′) — a verb meaning "to leave" • *dessert* — a noun meaning "the final course of a meal"	• Does Mexico have any **deserts**? • Why did Quetzalcoatl **desert** his kingdom? • What is a typical **dessert** after a Mexican meal?
• *lead* (lēd) — a verb that rhymes with *need,* meaning "to go first, to be a leader" • *led* — the past tense form of *lead,* meaning "went first" • *lead* (led) — a noun that rhymes with *bed,* meaning "a heavy metal; graphite used in pencils"	• Quetzalcoatl wanted to **lead** the people of Mexico. • He **led** the Toltecs in a Golden Age. • Was **lead** used by the Toltecs in their metalworking?
• *loose* (lo͞os) — an adjective that rhymes with *goose,* meaning "not tight" • *lose* (lo͞oz) — a verb meaning "to suffer loss"	• The cap on the bottle was **loose.** • The Toltecs were probably sad to **lose** their wise and kind ruler.

EXERCISE Proofreading a Paragraph

The following paragraph contains errors in the use of words that are easily confused. As you identify each error, cross out the word and write the correct word above it. One error has been identified and corrected as an example. Find and correct ten more.

The story of Quetzalcoatl is a myth. It tells about the ~~affect~~ *effect* that this great god of the sun

and the wind had on Mexico. He left the Land of the Sunrise and lead the Toltecs in a Golden

Age of prosperity. He was a wise and kind ruler who wanted the people to be happy. This

happy time lasted beyond the people's wildest dreams. They had peace, fulfilling work,

food, and prosperity. However, the neighboring states were very jealous. They wanted the

Toltecs to loose their happiness. They sent the chief of their gods, Tezcatlipoca, to play an

evil trick. He disguised himself and went to see Quetzalcoatl. He gave Quetzalcoatl wine,

which had a very bad affect on him. It was almost as if the wine had made his mind dessert

him. He could no longer led the country, and Tezcatlipoca took advantage of the situation.

He let lose magic arts that lead the people to destruction. His evil ways effected the whole

country. From the dessert to the valleys, the people were at war. Finally, the effects of the

wine wore off, and Quetzalcoatl was himself again. However, he was so upset that he de-

cided to leave the Toltecs. He burned their houses and buried his treasure in the valleys. The

happy days of the past were gone. The Toltecs felt the affects of his disappearance forever.

Ali Baba and the Forty Thieves
retold by Walter McVitty   **Pupil's Edition page 622**

Style: Words from Arabic and Other Languages

Picture this: Two friends are sitting on a <u>divan</u> sipping <u>lemon</u>-flavored ice water. They decide to order a plain cheese pizza. When the pizza arrives, it is covered with <u>spinach</u> and <u>peppers</u>. The driver had delivered the wrong pizza.

Although this scene sounds typically American, the underlined words actually had their beginnings in Indian and Middle-Eastern languages.

- *Divan* came from a Persian word.
- *Lemon* was first Persian, then Arabic, then French before becoming an English word.
- *Spinach,* too, has a long history but was originally Persian, then Arabic.
- *Peppers* began as a word in Sanskrit, the language of ancient India.

Words Borrowed from Arabic	
foods	artichoke, candy, saffron, alfalfa
furniture	sofa, mattress
cloth	muslin, cotton
mathematics	zero, algebra, average, cipher
valuable stones	lapis lazuli, amber

English isn't the only language that borrows words. Every word in every language has a history, and a word can be used by many languages before it reaches English. The history of a word is its **etymology.** For instance, the word *jar* came from the Old French word *jarre,* which came from the Spanish *jarra* and from the Arabic word *jarrah.* Dictionaries may show a word's etymology by using a symbol (<), which means "derived from" an earlier language. The languages mentioned in the etymology are often abbreviated. Dictionaries provide lists to explain their abbreviations.

> **jar:** [ME (Middle English) *jarre* < OF (Old French) *jarre* < Sp (Spanish) *jarra* < Ar (Arabic) *jarrah*]

As words move from language to language, they change spellings and pronunciations. Words can change meanings, too. For example, the English word *jungle* means "a thick, tropical forest." It comes from the Sanskrit word *jaṅgala,* which means "a desert."

EXERCISE A   Etymologies

Look up each of the following words in a dictionary that gives word histories. Then, on the line provided, write the languages named in the etymology of each word. Spell out the languages by using the abbreviations listed below or provided in the dictionary.

Ar = Arabic	MF or MFr = Middle French	Pers = Persian
It = Italian	OF or OFr = Old French	Sans or Skt = Sanskrit
ME = Middle English	OSp = Old Spanish	Turk = Turkish

EXAMPLE: **azure** Middle English < Old French < Arabic

1. sash (article of clothing) _____

2. khaki _____

3. turban _____

4. admiral _____

5. sugar _____

EXERCISE B **Exploring Word Meanings**

Use a dictionary to look up each of the following italicized words. Then, answer each question on the line provided.

EXAMPLE: From what Sanskrit word meaning "spotted" or "mottled" is the word *cheetah* derived?

Chitraka is the Sanskrit word from which cheetah is derived.

1. What is the meaning of the Arabic word from which the English word *syrup* is derived?

_____

2. The word *checkmate* (a term used in chess) is derived from the Persian "šāh māt." What is the translation of "šāh māt"?

_____

3. What does "brother" have to do with the word *pal*?

_____

4. From what Hindi word is the English word *cot*, meaning "a light, narrow bed," derived?

_____

5. In which language does the word for *average* mean "defective merchandise or wares"?

_____

EXERCISE C **Tracing Etymologies**

Look up the following words in a dictionary. Then, on the line provided, write the language from which the word was *first* derived.

EXAMPLE: pagoda Sanskrit

1. barrio _____

2. coffee _____

3. safari _____

4. bwana _____

5. Swahili _____

LANGUAGE LINK

The Emperor's New Clothes
Hans Christian Andersen

Pupil's Edition page 638

Style: Formal and Informal English

Why do kings and queens wear crowns and fancy robes? Kings and queens hold special places in society, and they want everyone to know they do! Like clothing, language has different styles. Notice the two styles of the sentences below:

> After they had tricked the king, they cheated him out of a fortune.

> After they'd done a number on the king's head, they ripped him off for a bundle.

The first sentence is written in **formal English.** Formal English is used when the occasion calls for a serious tone. Formal writing does not use contractions such as *they'd* or slang expressions such as *ripped him off.* Use formal English for most school writing assignments, speeches, and official correspondence. If you write your own fairy tale, however, you might use **informal English.** As in the second sentence above, informal English often includes contractions and colloquial expressions (colorful words and phrases of everyday conversation). Whatever the style, remember to be consistent.

EXERCISE A Identifying Formal and Informal English

Read each sentence below, and identify the style by writing an **I** (for informal) or an **F** (for formal) on the line provided. Then, on the line below the sentence, rewrite the sentence in the opposite style.

EXAMPLE: ___F___ Those swindlers certainly were very well prepared.

Those crooks really had their act together.

_____ **1.** On the one hand, the emperor in Hans Christian Andersen's story must have had sawdust for brains.

_____

_____

_____ **2.** On the other hand, those swindler dudes could've sold ice to penguins.

_____

_____

_____ **3.** The swindler's story was altogether false, but everyone believed it.

_____

_____

_____ **4.** Almost everyone pretended that he or she saw nothing amiss in the emperor's attire.

_____

_____

_____ **5.** The emperor's my name; fancy threads and duds are my game.

_____

_____

EXERCISE B **Proofreading Paragraphs**

In the paragraph below, rewrite any informal English that does not fit with the formal English used in the rest of the paragraph. One correction has been made as an example.

When I was younger, "The Emperor's New Clothes" ~~didn't make a lick of~~ *did not make any* sense to me. I wondered why the emperor is so foolish. Why does no one other than the child spill the beans about the emperor's clothes? Most importantly, why do the people put up with such a zero as their emperor?

Now that I've got a few years under my belt, the meaning of the story has become clearer. As children grow up, they learn to go along with the gang. People often don't put up with guys that rock the boat. As a result, it sometimes takes guts to go against the grain, and many people are content to let things slide.

The politicians in the story are not the only ones who pretend to see what they do not see. The whole town views the procession, yet everyone agrees on how cool the emperor's clothes look. They swallow the swindlers' lie, hook, line, and sinker. Only the child, less worried about what others think, is willing to be the first to blow the whistle.

He Lion, Bruh Bear, and Bruh Rabbit
retold by Virginia Hamilton   Pupil's Edition page 647

Proofreading: *To, Too,* and *Two*

Here's a riddle for you: When can two words sound the same but mean very different things? The answer: When they are **homophones,** like the words *to, too,* and *two.* Even though these three words are small, don't let them trick you. Here are some tips to help you know when to use these words and some other homophones correctly.

to	a preposition	*They went **to** the place where Man was.
too	an adverb meaning *also, more than enough*	*Bruh Bear went along, **too.**
two	one plus one	*The **two** animals went to see Bruh Bear.
hear	a verb meaning *to receive sounds through the ears*	*Everybody around he Lion could **hear** him roar.
here	an adverb meaning *in this place*	*He Lion is scaring everybody around **here.**
its	the possessive form of *it*	*Bruh Bear didn't fear the gun and **its** sting.
it's	a contraction of *it is* or *it has*	***It's** an interesting story.
plain	an adjective meaning *simple, clear;* a noun meaning a *flat area of land*	*He Lion knew the **plain** truth when he saw, heard, and felt it. *He Lion thought he was the king of valleys, hills, and **plains.**
plane	noun meaning a *flat surface,* a *tool,* an *airplane*	*A piece of paper is an example of a **plane.** *Carpenters smooth wood with a **plane.** *The Bruh Rabbit tales were first told long before **planes** flew through the air.

EXERCISE A   Choosing the Correct Word

Circle the word in parentheses that will make each sentence correct. Then, rewrite the sentence correctly on the line provided.

> **EXAMPLE:**   Bruh Bear and Bruh Rabbit went ((to), too, two) he Lion and talked with him.
> Bruh Bear and Bruh Rabbit went to he Lion and talked with him.

1. "What's all this noise I (hear, here)?" the little animals must have said at first.

   _____

2. The little animals and some big ones, (to, too, two), were upset by his racket.

   _____

3. They picked out (to, too, two) animals—Bruh Bear and Bruh Rabbit—as their ambassadors.

   _____

4. After Bruh Bear and Bruh Rabbit had talked with he Lion, it was (plain, plane) that he wouldn't pay them any mind.

_____

5. Anyway, (its, it's) rather difficult having a conversation with someone who only talks about himself.

_____

EXERCISE B   Using Confusing Words in Context

Complete each of the following sentences with two of the words below. Some words may be used in more than one sentence.

to	too	two	hear	here
its	it's	plain	plane	

1. Everybody around _____ can _____ him every morning.

2. Bruh Rabbit knew about the forest, and he knew about Man and where
   _____ find him, _____.

3. Suddenly, the _____ ran off _____ some bushes and hid.

4. _____ easy to understand the theme of this story and _____ moral.

5. One fact is _____: not one _____ appears in this folk tale.

EXERCISE C   Proofreading a Paragraph

The following paragraph contains errors in the use of homophones, or words that sound the same but have different meanings. As you identify each error, cross out the word and write the correct word above it. One error has been identified and rewritten as an example.

                   to
Many storytellers like ~~too~~ describe a contest between to opponents who are unevenly

matched. At the beginning, the outcome seems plane. Most people think that the one who is

stronger, bigger, or richer will be the winner. The future, however, is not always as plain as it

seems. Even though one of the opponents is an underdog, he or she usually outsmarts the

stronger one. This type of underdog is known as a trickster. It's easy to recognize a trickster

tale when you here it—it's story always involves someone being taken down a peg or two. In

the case of he Lion, no one in the valley or on the planes complains about his roaring anymore.

Collection One: Moments of Truth

Just Once, page 1

Exercise A

1. did
2. given
3. knew
4. made
5. seen

Exercise B

Some other linemen, like us, had also ~~gived~~ *given* some

thought to carrying the ball. We just stayed quiet

and ~~gone~~ *went* about our business. However, after the

Moose had ~~went~~ *gone* to the coach, we discussed the

issue. We ~~seen~~ *saw* both points of view—the coach's

and the Moose's.

We're glad that the Moose ~~gotten~~ *got* his chance

because it was our chance, too. Also, we have ~~came~~ *come*

to realize that everybody has something he or she

does best, and we're going to keep on blocking.

Ta-Na-E-Ka, page 3

Exercise A

1. are
2. demand
3. preserves
4. teach
5. were

Exercise B

(Corrections are shown in italics.)

Historically, the attitudes and traditions of many cultures *allow* for a different treatment of men and women, boys and girls. However, in "Ta-Na-E-Ka," we see a culture in which neither males nor females *receive* preferential treatment.

Roger's parents, Mary's parents, and Roger and Mary's grandfather *agree* that Ta-Na-E-Ka is an important tradition. Grandfather and the parents *need* to compromise, though, because they disagree on some parts of the tradition. They end up with a fair agreement.

Mary and Roger choose which part of the woods they will claim. Mary stays by the river while Roger goes into the woods. At that point, intelligence or traditions *become* the key to survival. In the end, Mary breaks with tradition, but Grandfather shows that both he and his traditions *are* flexible.

Exercise C

Answers will vary. Students' sentences should make sense and be complete. Correct verb numbers are listed below.

1. plural
2. plural
3. singular
4. plural

The All-American Slurp, page 5

Exercise A

Answers may vary but should make sense and include the correct verb choice. Possible answers are provided.

1. Eating rituals *are* different in different cultures because each culture has a unique history and circumstances.
2. The chopsticks *are* here in the drawer.
3. The parents *were* enjoying the meal.
4. The rice and prawns *are* on the stove.
5. I *have* never been embarrassed while eating.

Exercise B

Subject	Verb
1. food	is
2. Specialties	taste
3. Meals	differ
4. ingredients	are
5. food	is

Exercise C

(Corrections are shown in italics.)

Students in schools across the nation *get* embarrassed easily. *Has* an embarrassing thing happened to you? One of the most likely places *is* the cafeteria. Your friends tell jokes, sometimes right after you take a big swallow of milk. *Have* you ever dropped a tray full of food? The cafeteria in most schools *is* the stage of many such scenes. Sometimes accidents in a cafeteria *are* hazardous to your ego.

La Bamba, page 7

Exercise A

1. walked, past
2. kicks, present
3. had raised, past perfect
4. has practiced, present perfect
5. knew, past; had, past
6. will have seen, future perfect
7. laughs, present
8. will volunteer, future

9. had played, past perfect
10. will have graduated, future perfect

Exercise B
(Corrections are shown in italics.)

When I was in the sixth grade, I *performed* in a talent contest. I decided to play the school song on my guitar. I practiced almost every day before the show so that I *knew* the song as well as I knew my name. The night of the show, everybody except me *acted* nervous. I *walked* around backstage and tapped kids on the shoulders and they *jumped*. The first performer tap-danced in a red tutu. Halfway through the routine, one of her heels flew off. The dancer *kept* right on dancing. The second performer *was* Jamal, a buddy of mine. He read a few haiku that he wrote himself. He received a huge round of applause when he finished. Finally, I *heard* my name announced. I grabbed my guitar and jumped up on stage. Then I launched into the song. I took a deep breath. Just as I *was* ready to sing the first line, one of my strings broke, and it popped me on my upper lip. "Ow!" I *yelled*. People were stunned. After a few seconds, I started to sing, but my upper lip was numb, and only nonsense words came out! The audience did not know how to respond. I finally gave up and *stalked* off the stage.

President Cleveland, Where Are You?, page 9

Exercise A
1. risked — vivid
    threatened — vivid
2. went — vague
3. snorted — vivid
4. rode — vague
5. exploded — vivid

Exercise B
Answers will vary. Check to see that students have correctly identified the verbs in their paragraph. In the chart, students' vivid verbs should be suitable synonyms for vague verbs.

After trading with a partner, students should explain how the vivid verbs improve imagery and enable the reader to better understand the emotions of the characters.

The Stone, page 11

Exercise A
1. doesn't
2. doesn't
3. don't
4. don't
5. don't

Exercise B
1. is
2. buys
3. doesn't
4. is
5. is

Exercise C
(Corrections appear in italics.)

"I *don't* understand why you don't want the stone any longer, Maibon."

"My wife *doesn't* like the way I *am* now that I have power over my aging. The kids *are* scared of me, too. They *don't* understand why they and their mother keep growing older while I don't get any older at all."

"I'll tell you what I am willing to do since you *are* in such a predicament. *Little Sellers Weekly* *is* a newspaper the Fair Folk put out each week. I *don't* know of a better place to run an ad for the stone. We *are* going to tell the virtues of the stone and set the price at one thousand dollars."

"One thousand dollars *is* a fortune! I *don't* think we are going to get a buyer with that price, but we are going to have to try. The ad is our only hope."

Collection Two: Unforgettable Personalities

Storm, page 13

Exercise A
1. good
2. well
3. well
4. good
5. good

Exercise B
(Corrections are shown in italics.)

I have another *good* story about my dog Storm. We had just done really *well* in a big race, and I was exhausted. I had been sick for several days and still was not feeling *well*. I sat in a big, comfortable chair in the corner of my cabin. I had built a fire that did a good job of keeping me warm. As I sat and tried to rest, I heard a rustling at the window. I did not feel good about the sound. The wind howled. I quietly called out, "Storm? Storm? Are you there?"

I waited silently, and I looked through the window. I saw a brown stocking cap moving outside. The wind moaned, and I had a sinking feeling inside me. The situation was not *good*. Suddenly, Storm came through the door, giving me a good scare. He held my hunting hat in his mouth. I had a good laugh. It was only Storm outside playing a prank. He had certainly tricked me *well*. I was relieved, so I got out of my chair and went to the kitchen. I got Storm a treat. He had earned it *well*.

Brother, page 15

Exercise A

(Responses will vary. Sample responses follow.)

pretty	small
1. handsome	**7.** tiny
2. stunning	**8.** trivial

nice	fast
3. enchanting	**9.** swift
4. warmhearted	**10.** hasty

 cute

5. adorable
6. attractive

Exercise B

(Replacement words will vary. A sample response follows.)

I think that my brother Bailey is a *clever* person. He is very coordinated. He can steal pickles from the store when no one is looking. One time Momma caught him with his hand in the pickle barrel. She asked him, "Bailey, what are you doing at the pickle barrel?"

Bailey gulped. He thought quickly. "The *elegant* lady over by that *lanky* man asked for a pickle. I just wanted to help her."

Momma knew that Bailey was lying. Momma is also clever. The woman paid for her groceries. Momma packed everything the woman bought into one *enormous* bag. She then asked Bailey, "Bailey, why don't you help Mrs. Coleman carry her groceries up that *steep* hill?" Bailey's eyes got *gigantic*. Momma certainly knew how to deal with Bailey.

The Mysterious Mr. Lincoln, page 17

Exercise A
1. better

2. more
3. least
4. highest
5. less

Exercise B

(Corrections are shown in italics.)

Abraham Lincoln was one of the *greatest* presidents that this country has ever had. He led this country through one of the *most difficult* times in its history. Lincoln made two of the *most important* contributions to the country: preserving the Union and abolishing slavery.

Although Lincoln was against slavery, it was not until after the war began that he thought ending slavery was the *most important* of all war objectives. He issued the Emancipation Proclamation, which officially freed many slaves. Unfortunately, soon after the war, Lincoln was killed. The man who, during the war, was the *most unpopular* president of all time has come to be considered one of the *best* presidents in U.S. history.

A Glory over Everything, page 19

Exercise A
1. *Bad* modifies *situation.*
2. *Badly* modifies *wanted.*
3. *Bad* modifies *idea.*
4. *Bad* modifies *Tubman.*
5. *Badly* modifies *thought.*

Exercise B

(Corrections are shown in italics.)

After Tubman made her way to Pennsylvania, she still had much work to do. She wanted very *badly* to help other slaves achieve their freedom. However, she had to leave her husband and brothers behind, and she missed them *badly*. When she remembered them, she often felt *bad* about her decision. She also knew if she had remained in the South, she would have been separated from her husband and family as well. Owners often treated enslaved families *badly* and separated family members from each other.

Tubman went to work for the Underground Railroad. She helped many people escape slavery. Tubman hated slavery for many reasons. Not only were people often left in *bad* physical condition, but they were also not treated like human beings. Tubman admired the abolitionists, who believed that slavery was bad and worked to end it. In the end, Tubman helped many slaves who wanted to escape *badly*. No doubt Tubman saved many lives in her fight to free herself and others.

Collection Three: Machine Mania: People and Technology

The Fun They Had, page 21

Exercise A

1. Margie hated school**!** **She** was doing worse and worse in geography**.**
2. Where did Tommy find the book**?** **He** told Margie he found it in the attic**.**
3. The inspector came to fix the teacher**.** **Why** didn't he just take the teacher away**?**
4. How could a person be a teacher**?** **The** person must be smart**!**
5. Kids went to school in a special building**.** **They** could talk to each other**.**

NOTE: Periods in place of the exclamation points in sentences 1 and 4 would also be correct.

Exercise B

(Corrections are shown in large boldface.)

Margie was so excited**!** Tommy had found a real book. It seemed funny to hold a book in their hands**.** **They** were used to reading books on a screen. Tommy had found the book in the attic. It was a very old book, with yellowed pages.

What did Tommy and Margie read about in the book**?** **They** discovered that the book was about school. Margie couldn't understand why anyone would write about school. She hated school! It was so boring to sit alone in her room all day. The book said the teacher was a man. Margie's teacher was a machine.

The county inspector came to Margie's house to fix the mechanical teacher. He brought a box of tools and an apple for Margie**.** **He** took the teacher apart. Margie was so disappointed when he fixed the teacher**!** **She** was hoping he would take it away for a long time**.**

What was school really like back then**?** Margie imagined all the kids together. She sighed as she thought about it. What fun they must have had**!**

Collection Four: All Creatures Great and Small

Zlateh the Goat, page 23

Exercise A

1. he
2. her
3. him or her
4. It
5. she
6. he or she
7. It
8. she
9. him
10. his or her

Exercise B

"Zlateh the Goat" is a wonderful story about a

boy and *his* goat. At the beginning of the story,

Aaron, the boy, is told to sell Zlateh to the butcher.

Aaron doesn't really want to, but *he* does not want

to disobey *his* father. When Aaron and Zlateh set out

for the village on a sunny morning, Zlateh wonders

where Aaron is taking *her.* However, Zlateh trusts

Aaron and allows *him* to lead *her* along. When the

weather turns stormy, the two of them fear that *they*

are in danger. Luckily, Aaron finds shelter and food for

both of them. The two stay in *their* shelter for three

days. Many of the people in the town think Aaron is

lost in the storm, and *they* doubt he will survive.

When Aaron and Zlateh return, the family

members decide that *they* will never again

consider selling *their* goat.

Stray, page 25

Exercise A

1. who's
2. your
3. its
4. It's
5. You're
6. Whose
7. they're
8. who's
9. its
10. their

Exercise B

(Corrections are shown in italics.)

It's delightful to see the special relationship that exists between a child and a dog. The child, whose youthful energy knows no bounds, has a constant and loyal companion. *They're* always together—on walks, watching TV, even sleeping at night. Parents, *whose* concerns are mostly practical, often have to remind children to care for their dogs. *It's their* duty to say things like "Feed *your* dog." Although the parents may have to provide such reminders often, their hearts are warmed to see child and pet happily at play.

The Flood, page 27

Exercise A

1. clear
2. unclear, Frank Lamping or Ralph
3. unclear, trainers or animals
4. unclear, animal or cage
5. clear

Exercise B

(Sentences will vary. Sample responses follow.)

1. Bob had taken Clarence to the raging stream. Clarence dared not jump across.
2. Ralph was fumbling with the key to the cage, but the key fell into the water.
3. Toni and Ralph saw a lion and other animals on the top of a hill. The animals did not run away.
4. Miguel and Ralph talked. Miguel was using some English words and some Spanish words.
5. Did Toni see Modoc when Modoc was pulling the cages out of the water?

from *The Land I Lost,* page 29

Exercise A

1. IO
2. DO
3. OP
4. DO
5. OP

Exercise B

1. her
2. her
3. him
4. me
5. us

Exercise C

(Corrections are shown in italics.)

After many long years, Trung and Lan are finally to be married. They happily prepare for the day. To welcome Lan, Trung's family holds a dinner for *her.* The wedding is beautiful. Trung and Lan are very much in love and their mothers are happy for *them.* Later, tragedy strikes. While Lan is bathing in the river, a wily old crocodile attacks *her.* When Lan does not return from the river, Trung worries about *her.* It seems as if she and Trung will have to say goodbye to happiness. Fortunately, she outwits the crocodile and is able to escape from *it.* Lan signals to Trung, and she is reunited with *him.*

from *All I Really Need to Know I Learned in Kindergarten,* page 31

Exercise A

1. c   2. b   3. b

Exercise B

(Answers will vary. Sample responses follow.)

1. He is very, very fast.
2. I am very hungry. I could eat a large amount.
3. She's extremely tall.
4. It's very hot outside.
5. You look beautiful!

Exercise C

(Answers will vary. Sample responses follow.)

1. The bee flew away faster than a screeching jet fighter.
2. Her house is old enough to have belonged to a dinosaur.
3. She thought the bee looked like an elephant with wings.
4. Her stereo is so loud that it broke my eardrums.
5. He ran as fast as a cheetah on rollerskates.

Collection Five: Justice for All

All Summer in a Day, page 33

Exercise A

1. **S;** When she reads a science-fiction story, she feels as if she is being taken to visit another universe, where the familiar rules of gravity, motion, and time are altered.
2. **P;** Geoffrey was amazed to sense the sun's warm hand, stroking his face with its kind, gentle beams.
3. **M;** Margot became a wilted flower as she sat locked in the closet.
4. **P;** When the rain began to fall, the children's hearts sank, and they saw the bleak, gray clouds glaring at them in the sky.
5. **S;** "You're just like monsters," the teacher scolded. "Ganging up on Margot that way was a terrible thing to do."

Exercise B

(Answers will vary. Sample answers follow.)

1. Margot pressed her hands against the locked closet door; it *seemed to push back with painful, unseen hands.*

2. With the sun's rays warming the jungle, the sun looked *like a stranger with a magnificent, unknown face* to the children of Venus.
3. My sister has never known any place except this colony on Venus. To me this planet is like a wet, lifeless rag, but to her it's a *bountiful and caring mother*.
4. The ocean was so mysterious and lovely that it *sang like a lost love I would never forget.*
5. Jamal watered the dry rosebush, and when he was finished, the bush *stretched out its shiny leaves and dark blossoms in an ecstasy of gratitude.*

Exercise C

Paragraphs will vary but should contain at least five figures of speech, including similes, metaphors, and personification.

Eleven / Once, page 35

Exercise A

1. a
2. b
3. a
4. a
5. a

Exercise B

(Changes are circled and in boldface.)

Rachel used to look forward to her upcoming birthdays. When she turned eight, she couldn't wait. "**I**t's so much fun to have a party and a big cake**,**" she told her cousin Marta. Actually, when she thinks about it now, many of her birthdays have been letdowns, disappointing days when she felt as though she were a punctured tire with the air leaking out.

She called Marta and asked, "**D**oes it feel different when you become a teenager?**"** Marta was two years older, and she seemed to know everything. Rachel thought it was a shame that she couldn't catch up with her cousin. When Marta was eleven, Rachel was only nine. Now that Rachel was finally becoming eleven herself, Marta was still ahead of her, of course. Thirteen and proud of it!

Rachel asked her, "**I**s it fun to be thirteen?**"**

"Well,**"** Marta replied, **"**it's not bad. You get to do some things you couldn't do as a child."

"Like what?**"** asked Rachel.

"Having a job, for one thing!**"** Marta said. "I spent all last weekend baby-sitting!"

The Gold Cadillac, page 37

Exercise A

(Responses will vary in word choice. Sample responses are provided.)

1. __P__ 'Lois and her sister were surprised by their mother's *stubborn* refusal to ride in the Cadillac.

2. __N__ 'Lois's mother thought it was *daring* for her husband to buy an expensive car.

3. __P__ After the Cadillac was sold, the family rode in an *old* Ford.

4. __P__ 'Lois thought her ride through the South in the *gaudy* Cadillac would remain a memory forever.

5. __N__ The signs that 'Lois saw in the windows of restaurants and motels made her *nosy*.

Exercise B

1. +   3. −   5. +
   −   +   −
2. +   4. −
   −   +

The Bracelet, page 39

Exercise A

(Revisions appear in boldface type.)

1. "Yolanda told me that she heard Mr. Méndez say, **'**Your book reports are due on Friday.**'**"
2. "The sportscaster on the news said, **'**The game has been canceled on account of bad weather,**'**" said Sal.
3. **C**
4. "The doctor said, **'**It's a healthy baby girl!**'**" shouted Eli as he entered the waiting room.
5. "When we arrived at the museum, Mrs. Govea said, **'**Enjoy the tour, but stay together,**'**" said Miki, reminding us of our instructions.

Exercise B

(Paragraph changes are shown correctly. Added quotation marks are circled.)

Nancy said, "Thomas and I were wondering where Keiko and Ruri live now."

"I don't know,**"** Laurie replied, "but I really miss my best friend. I wonder if Ruri is thinking about me, too."

Mama had done wonders in making the little stall seem more like home. "Look at the way she's brightened up the place!" Keiko declared.

"I think it looks very nice," Ruri replied. "Still, I miss our real home."

"I know it's difficult for you children," said Mama, **"**but at least we have each other.**"**

"That's true," said Keiko. Ruri was still silent.

"What's the matter, honey?" asked Mama. **"**You still look very sad; maybe you should tell us what's wrong.**"**

Ruri murmured, "I wish I could cry, but I feel too scared and numb. I wanted to keep my promise to Laurie about the bracelet. I said I wasn't ever going to take the bracelet off, so I could look at it and keep her with me."

"She is with you, in your heart," Mama explained, "just as your father and I are joined together, even though we can't see each other. Remembering someone you care for is the most important thing."

What Do Fish Have to Do with Anything?, page 41

Exercise A

1. I
2. Mrs. Markham asked, "Willie, have you seen a movie about fish or something?"
3. Willie replied, "I've seen the movie *Free Willy,* but it's about a whale, not a fish."
4. I

5. Willie said, "I'd rather have a whale be my friend than have a whole big bag full of money."

Exercise B

1. The man explained to Willie that people always need a little extra.
2. Caroline explained that she felt disappointed when she discovered that adults didn't have all the answers, either.
3. Willie said that it's hard when they tell you not to ask questions.
4. Mrs. Markham said she came to pick up her son because she feels parents must protect their children.
5. Tina asked Willie whether he had seen the man who used to beg on their street. She wondered where he'd gone.

Collection Seven: Explaining Our World: Fact and Fiction

Loo-Wit, the Fire-Keeper, page 43

Exercise A

1. foxes
2. loaves
3. cheeses
4. monkeys
5. taxes
6. patios
7. men
8. toys
9. mice
10. puppies
11. gulfs
12. rashes
13. pianos
14. moose
15. strawberries

Exercise B

(Answers will vary. A sample response is provided. The five plural nouns appear in italics.)

"Loo-Wit, the Fire-Keeper" is a story about two *brothers*. They are both *chiefs* of their own *peoples*. Even though they are brothers, their *lives* become complicated by the jealousy and envy that they have for each other. They each seem to want what the other has. In the end, they do not resolve their conflict and are turned into two mountains reaching up into the *skies*.

from *Volcano*, page 45

Exercise A

1. The goldfish looked up at me with sad, lonely eyes.
2. The extreme heat and the explosions of the volcano created flames that danced through the trees.
3. The mouth of the volcano yawned wide as it released a horrendous burst of gas and fire.
4. The tremendous winds angrily snatched my hat from my hand.
5. The sun smiled with comfort upon the surviving wildlife.

Exercise B

1. X
2. P; The mudflows raced over the injured landscape.
3. X
4. P; Mount St. Helens stands head and shoulders above adjacent peaks in the Cascade Range.
5. P; When the eruptions stopped, scientists wondered whether the plant life would return, and whether nature would heal itself after its suffering.

Exercise C

(Answers will vary. Sample responses follow.)

1. Hot ash poured from the volcano's peak and clothed the town in scorching apparel.
2. Lancelot discovered that the computer was being stubborn again.
3. On the news, we saw some photographs taken from inside the belly of a deep volcanic crater.
4. Hot magma boils inside the earth's crust, a secret passion seething in its heart.
5. Nora searched for a pair of pliers, but she discovered that they had walked away from the place she had put them last.

The Seventh Sister, page 47

Exercise A

1. I think there is nothing so lovely as the sight of a pair of bright, glowing stars in the sky.
2. When can we hear the story about Chang's sweet, sorrowful love songs?
3. C
4. He approaches the silver reflecting pond, and he sees the enchanted, shimmering magpie feather he wants.
5. C

Exercise B

(Added commas appear in boldface.)

People from many different cultures have told stories about the stars in the sky, yet nobody has ever explained their origin completely. The mythological stories of the ancient Greeks are full of vengeful**,** irresponsible gods and goddesses. Many of these gods and goddesses place their monsters or favorite heroes in the starry sky. One such hero is the strong**,** valiant**,** ill-treated Hercules. Hercules suffered from the jealousy of devious**,** sly Hera, who was the queen of all the gods.

The Chinese myth of the Seventh Sister gives an endearing explanation. Chang and Mei are placed in the sky to preserve their enduring love. They are allowed to be united once a year. At all other times Mei must be occupied with her beautiful tapestry making. Chang and Mei are a pair of glorious**,** brilliant stars, yet they are separated most of the year by a galaxy called the Milky Way. These patient**,** tender sweethearts are as brave as the mighty Hercules in their own way.

Scanning the Heavens, page 49

Exercise A

(If you permit students to omit the final series comma, then the commas that are underscored in the following exercises may be considered optional.)

1. Chinese astronomers measured the orbits of celestial bodies, predicted natural events, and recorded celestial phenomena.
2. Farmers, philosophers, priests, and kings were all interested in learning about the stars.
3. The astronomers were able to predict changing seasons, tidal conditions, eclipses, and other events on earth by studying the stars and planets.
4. Through an examination of their scientific practices, writing skills, calendars, and records of the natural world, modern scholars have found evidence that the ancient Chinese were an advanced civilization.
5. How long ago did the emperor Huang-Ti teach the people to raise silkworms, collect the silken fibers, use a calligraphic system of writing, and play music?

Exercise B

Modern scientists were astounded when they began to examine the cultural, artistic, and astronomical knowledge of ancient Chinese civilization. Long before there were high-powered telescopes, weather satellites, or other modern tools, Chinese astronomers were able to calculate an accurate calendar by observing the heavens. They also understood that orbits of celestial bodies could be monitored, measured, and understood by close observation. When Marco Polo visited Beijing in the thirteenth century, he encountered a population of avid, knowledgeable stargazers.

Five hundred years before astronomers in the West, Chinese scientists began to predict, study, and observe the appearance of lunar eclipses, solar eclipses, comets, and novas. Novas were called guest stars; they lasted only two days, appearing bright at first, then rapidly burning out and exploding just before disappearing from sight.

How the Snake Got Poison, page 51

Exercise A

1. I	3. F	5. F
2. I	4. I	

Exercise B

(Answers will vary. Sample responses follow.)

1. SKUNK: "What's up, Snake? Can we have a little talk?"
2. SNAKE: "Sure as shootin', Skunk. You're looking tippy-top. What's goin' on?"
3. SKUNK: "Well, the problem is I stink."
4. SNAKE: "I get it."
5. SKUNK: "I've had it! I'm fed up! No one wants to hang out with me."
6. SNAKE: "Whadya wanna smell like?"
7. SKUNK: "Something kinda classy. This skunk business is for the birds! People see me coming, and they run the other way, you know what I mean?"

Collection Eight: Tell Me a Tale

Medusa's Head, page 53

Exercise A

1. Tantalus	4. Proteus
2. Titans	5. Atlas
3. Hercules	

Exercise B

1. titanic	4. atlas
2. tantalize	5. protean
3. herculean	

Exercise C

1. protean	4. atlas
2. tantalize	5. titanic
3. herculean	

Exercise D

(Answers will vary. Students should have a reasonable explanation for each word.)

Baucis and Philemon, page 55

Exercise A

1. There
2. Their, peace
3. week
4. Your
5. Their

Exercise B

(Corrections are shown in italics.)

With no hotels or restaurants, hospitality was important to the Greeks. The custom was for people to share *their* homes and food with travelers. Of course, *there* are different ways to show hospitality. Some people would share only the best of what they had, treating strangers like honored guests. Others might share only the bare necessities. Still others might refuse to share at all. They might say, "We've got a sick relative here who is too *weak* to move. Take *your* request to another house."

Baucis and Philemon would never refuse to help a stranger. Even though they were poor, this couple was eager to help. When Zeus and Hermes knocked on their door, they immediately began to treat *their* guests generously. Only their best would do for these guests. Instead of serving one *piece* of fruit, Baucis put out many different kinds. The gods were deeply touched by their kindness.

"*Your* hospitality has not gone unnoticed," they said. They asked the elderly couple to choose *their* reward. Philemon asked that *their* cottage be transformed into a temple. They wanted to continue to live in *peace* for the rest of their lives.

Philemon asked that they be allowed to die at the same time. *Their* love was so strong that they couldn't stand to be apart. So week after week, the two lived happily together. Finally, when they became too weak to stand, the gods transformed them into two beautiful trees.

Quetzalcoatl, page 57

Exercise

(Corrections are shown in italics.)

The story of Quetzalcoatl is a myth. It tells about the *effect* that this great god of the sun and the wind had on Mexico. He left the Land of the Sunrise and *led* the Toltecs in a Golden Age of prosperity. He was a wise and kind ruler who wanted the people to be happy. This happy time lasted beyond the people's wildest dreams. They had peace, fulfilling work, food, and prosperity. However, the neighboring states were very jealous. They wanted the Toltecs to *lose* their happiness. They sent the chief of their gods, Tezcatlipoca, to play an evil trick. He disguised

himself and went to see Quetzalcoatl. He gave Quetzalcoatl wine, which had a very bad *effect* on him. It was almost as if the wine had made his mind *desert* him. He could no longer *lead* the country, and Tezcatlipoca took advantage of the situation. He let *loose* magic arts that *led* the people to destruction. His evil ways *affected* the whole country. From the *desert* to the valleys, the people were at war. Finally, the effects of the wine wore off, and Quetzalcoatl was himself again. However, he was so upset that he decided to leave the Toltecs. He burned their houses and buried his treasure in the valleys. The happy days of the past were gone. The Toltecs felt the *effects* of his disappearance forever.

Ali Baba and the Forty Thieves, page 59

Exercise A

(Answers may vary. Check answers using students' dictionaries.)

1. sash—Arabic
2. khaki—Hindi < Persian
3. turban—Middle French < Italian < Turkish
4. admiral—Middle English < Old French < Arabic
5. sugar—Middle English < Old French < Old Spanish < Arabic < Persian < Sanskrit

Exercise B

(Answers may vary. Check answers using students' dictionaries.)

1. The Arabic word *shariba* means "to drink." *Sharab* means "a drink."
2. *Šāh māt* means "the king is dead."
3. *Pal* comes from Romany and Sanskrit words meaning "brother."
4. *khat*
5. Arabic

Exercise C

(Answers may vary. Check answers using students' dictionaries.)

1. Arabic
2. Arabic
3. Arabic
4. Arabic
5. Arabic

The Emperor's New Clothes, page 61

Exercise A

(Revisions will vary. Sample revisions follow.)

1. I; From one point of view, the emperor in Hans Christian Andersen's story must have been a very gullible man.
2. I; From the other point of view, the swindlers could have sold anything to anybody.

3. F; The swindlers' story was totally bogus, but everyone bought it.
4. F; Just about everyone made like the emperor's clothes were fine and dandy.
5. I; I am the emperior; I must have fine clothes.

Exercise B

(Revisions will vary. Sample responses follow.)

When I was younger, "The Emperor's New Clothes" ~~didn't make a lick of~~ [did not make any] sense to me. I wondered why the emperor is so foolish. Why does no one other than the child ~~spill the beans~~ [tell the truth] about the emperor's clothes? Most importantly, why do the people ~~put up with such a zero~~ [accept such a foolish man] as their emperor?

Now that ~~I've got a few years under my belt~~ [I am older], the meaning of the story has become clearer. As children grow up, they learn to ~~go along with the gang~~ [fit in with others]. People often ~~don't put up with guys that rock the boat~~ [do not tolerate those who rebel]. As a result, it ~~sometimes takes guts to go against the grain~~ [is sometimes risky to raise objections], and many people are content to ~~let things slide~~ [remain silent].

The politicians in the story are not the only ones who pretend to see what they do not see. The whole town views the procession, yet everyone agrees on how ~~cool~~ [marvelous] the emperor's clothes look. They ~~swallow~~ [completely accept] the swindlers' lie, ~~hook, line, and sinker~~. Only the child, less worried about what others think, is willing to be the first to ~~blow the whistle~~ [speak the truth].

He Lion, Bruh Bear, and Bruh Rabbit, page 63

Exercise A

1. hear
2. too
3. two
4. plain
5. it's

Exercise B

1. here, hear
2. to, too
3. two, to
4. It's, its
5. plain, plane

Exercise C

Many storytellers like ~~too~~ [to] describe a contest between ~~to~~ [two] opponents who are unevenly matched. At the beginning, the outcome seems ~~plane~~ [plain]. Most people think that the one who is stronger, bigger, or richer will be the winner. The future, however, is not always as plain as it seems. Even though one of the opponents is an underdog, he or she usually outsmarts the stronger one. This type of underdog is known as a trickster. It's easy to recognize a trickster tale when you ~~here~~ [hear] it—~~it's~~ [its] story always involves someone being taken down a peg or two. In the case of he Lion, no one in the valley or on the ~~planes~~ [plains] complains about his roaring anymore.